Praise for *TRICARE Around the World*

"Indispensable resource for military families, retirees, and avid travelers . . . Answers the most pressing questions about obtaining medical care while overseas or when traveling across the USA. A must-read for any member of the military community."

Stephanie Montague, chief editor of
Poppin' Smoke military travel blog

"Simplifies TRICARE for <u>everyone</u> (all military families, not just expat ones) . . . The claims checklist alone is well worth the price of the book."

Doug Nordman, author of *The Military Guide to
Financial Independence and Retirement*

"Even the TRICARE site is not organized this well. Gives detailed step-by-step procedures and many times also explains why they are so critical to follow."

Robert R. Crawford, Amazon reviewer

"I worked for the TRICARE program for 20 years, and I would highly recommend this book to all TRICARE beneficiaries."

Mikahela, Amazon reviewer

"As a recently retired US Army Reservist Family Practice physician, I have been asked by patients how to best use TRICARE. This book serves to demystify the process . . . The detailed instructions on how TRICARE works . . . and potential pitfalls make this book worth its price many times over . . . Understandable for those new to using TRICARE . . . For retired military members, this book is a must".

Robert S., TRICARE beneficiary and physician

"Excellent information in one place . . . gives you the confidence to make it all work."

Rob141, USAF (retired), Amazon reviewer

D1453793

All information is believed to be accurate at the time of publishing. For inquiries or corrections, contact John@theTRICAREguy.com.

This book is available at special discount for non-profits, promotions, or premiums. Special editions, including tailored covers with corporate imprints, can be created for bulk purchase.

Editor: Jennifer L. Jansons
Cover art: Andrea Schmidt (www.a-schmidt.com)
Back cover photo by Meleia

ISBN: Paperback: 978-1-7367116-2-0
          E-book: 978-1-7367116-3-7

First edition: April 2021
Second edition: March 2022

Publisher's Cataloging-In-Publication Data

Names: Letaw, John D., author.
Title: TRICARE around the world : getting the most from your
    military medical benefits / John D. Letaw.
Description: Second edition. | [Kailua, Hawaii] : [Deep Blue C
    Press], 2022.
Identifiers: ISBN 9781736711620 (paperback) | ISBN
    9781736711637 (ebook)
Subjects: LCSH: Managed care plans (Medical care)--United
    States--Handbooks, manuals, etc. | United States. Office of the
    Assistant Secretary of Defense (Health Affairs). TRICARE
    Management Activity--Handbooks, manuals, etc. | United
    States--Armed Forces--Medical care--Handbooks, manuals, etc.
    | Travel--Health aspects. | LCGFT: Handbooks and manuals.
Classification: LCC RA413.5.U5 L48 2022 (print) | LCC RA413.5.U5
    (ebook) | DDC 362.1042580973--dc23

TRICARE® Around the World:

Getting the Most from Your Military Medical Benefits

Second Edition

Dedication

This book is for the men and women of the armed forces: Past, present, and future.

For their families, loved ones, and caregivers.

Thank you for your service to our nation and to one another. This book is our contribution to help make your journey easier.

TRICARE® Around the World:

Getting the Most from Your Military Medical Benefits

Second Edition

☆   ☆   ☆

J. D. LETAW

The following are trademarks of their respective holders. The author does not claim any affiliation or rights to these trademarked names, logos, wordmarks, products, or services:

At the time of publication, this information is believed to be current and accurate. TRICARE policies and benefits are governed by public law and federal regulations. Changes to TRICARE programs are continually made as public law and/or federal regulations are amended. Policies of individual military hospitals, clinics and providers may differ from those outlined in this publication.

Nothing in this book should be construed as medical advice. For the most up-to-date information, contact your TRICARE regional contractor, local military hospital or clinic, or visit www.tricare.mil.

Table of Contents

Preface

THE FIRST EDITION OF THIS BOOK was written in Hua Hin, Thailand, in 2020. My wife, daughter, and I had just completed two years living in Japan, and we had grand plans of global travel in the coming year. Hua Hin was the first stop in this journey, but then the COVID-19 pandemic lockdown changed everything. We found ourselves in that small town for the next 18 months with no friends or family nearby.

This unexpected period of isolation provided the perfect time to write. *TRICARE Around the World* drew on our experiences as a retiree family living overseas as well as the collective stories of users in our TRICARE social media group.

In June 2021, we returned to the U.S. where I began work on the second edition. This was the first time we had enrolled in TRICARE Select in the States; our prior stateside experience had been with TRICARE Prime. As before, the book is influenced by our personal experience combined with deep research of official sources. With the added perspective of a family using TRICARE in the U.S. and new first-hand stories, this is a resource for active duty families, retirees, and all TRICARE users across the country and around the globe.

This book and our social media groups share a common goal: To educate and inform the military community about getting the most from your TRICARE benefits wherever you go. We invite you to read, learn, and ask questions with others who are on the same quest. Visit **www.theTRICAREguy.com** to connect with our very supportive online community. We hope to cross paths with you one day and share stories of our worldwide adventures!

John D. Letaw
Kailua, Hawaii
March, 2022

Disclaimer

THE AUTHOR IS NOT and never has been an employee or representative of TRICARE, Military Health System, or any TRICARE contractor. This publication is not sponsored by, affiliated with, or endorsed by the U.S. government nor has it been reviewed by any government agency.

Military medical benefits and costs are subject to change at any time, often with little or no notice. This can happen through legislation or by issuance of rules by appropriate authority. Information herein is believed to be accurate at the time of publication. Changes may have occurred since publication and may not be reflected in this book.

This book is for educational purposes only. It is not intended as, and should not be construed as, medical advice or a definitive statement or commitment of benefits. The reader should verify critical information with their TRICARE provider or regional contractor. The author assumes no liability for inaccurate, incomplete, or outdated information in this book, nor for any inferences or conclusions that might be drawn from it.

Foreword

Benito N. Cuevas

I AM A FORMER TRICARE OVERSEAS CUSTOMER SERVICE REPRESENTATIVE with nearly twenty years of claims experience before my retirement in April 2021. I am also a U.S. Army veteran but not a TRICARE beneficiary myself. During my tenure with the TRICARE Overseas program, I assisted countless service members, families, and retirees with their claim inquiries. I met John Letaw through his TRICARE support Facebook group, *TRICARE Around the World,* in 2021. This group hosts thousands of members who share their vast knowledge and experience with one another. I felt that by joining the group I could provide useful insight about the claims process used by TRICARE Overseas and in doing so assist members to resolve their claims issues. It is an honor to continue assisting TRICARE beneficiaries in this way.

The TRICARE program can be a very complicated benefit to navigate. Although there are numerous websites that provide information on the program, they are not always helpful or easy to understand. John Letaw's *TRICARE Around the World* is an extremely well-organized book. He has done an amazing job of gathering the most relevant TRICARE policies and information into one compact resource. His writing style is easy to understand and cuts through the bureaucratic jargon so often used in government programs. The material is well laid out in a very logical way.

On the Kindle version, I found the hyperlinks to be extremely helpful for looking up the source material tied directly to online resources. I was very impressed by how this book covers the various TRICARE programs and presents the benefits and care options. While no one book can possibly cover every specific question about the TRICARE program, I believe that *TRICARE Around the World* does a fantastic job of covering the bases.

Now in its second edition, I highly recommend this book whether you are active duty or retired. If I was still with TRICARE Overseas, I would suggest this book to every beneficiary that called in for assistance. Having this book on hand could prove to be a very beneficial resource, especially if one is traveling.

Benito N. Cuevas
TRICARE Overseas Customer Service Representative
(Retired)

Author's Note:
Acronyms

ANYONE WHO HAS BEEN AROUND the military for any length of time knows that military speech is full of jargon and acronyms. This can be overwhelming to the newcomer because it seems like everyone around you is speaking a foreign language. We are sensitive to this throughout the book, and we believe that a large part of our mission is to educate our audience so that we can all participate more fully in discussions about health care.

It is hard to have an informed conversation on any topic of complexity without some degree of fluency among the participants. For this reason, acronyms used in this book are explained in their first usage and again from time to time. As you read this book, we hope that you will deepen your understanding of the vocabulary involved.

As an aid to our readers, **Appendix B at the back of the book has a complete list of acronyms.** This may well be the most complete list of TRICARE-related acronyms anywhere. Bookmark Appendix B and refer to it often.

1
Getting Started

THIS BOOK IS THE RESULT OF DECADES OF EXPERIENCE traveling, living overseas, and using TRICARE both as an active duty family and in retirement. Since 2019, we have been leading a vibrant and growing community of TRICARE users on Facebook. While the thousands of stories shared in that group give us deep insight into TRICARE in its many forms, it has long been our goal to branch out beyond social media to reach even more of the military community. This book fulfills that dream.

Living in Thailand in 2020, the sudden pandemic lockdown presented a unique opportunity to write this book. The following year, we returned to Hawaii where this second edition was written. In earlier times, we lived in Japan as SOFA contractors, with access to military health care and later in a non-SOFA status where we relied on Japanese doctors. These various settings have given us a broad perspective of TRICARE, both stateside and internationally, which we share with you in this book.

This expanded edition goes deeper than ever with:

- More expert tips and real-life stories that illustrate the use of TRICARE benefits in practical terms
- Obtaining VA benefits, even without a VA disability rating
- How Medicare and TRICARE for Life work together, along with a discussion of Medicare Advantage and Medicare supplements
- Additional insight for family members with special needs, including life-long care for adult children with disabilities
- Updates on ever-changing TRICARE plans so that you and your family can stay current with your benefits.

TRICARE Around the World

With extensive links to official government sources and based on the experiences of thousands of users worldwide, *TRICARE Around the World* is the broadest look ever at one of America's largest health plans.

TRICARE: A Life Skill

Just like learning to swim, mastering TRICARE is a skill that you can acquire, but it requires focus and intentionality. You would not teach yourself to swim by recklessly jumping into the deep end of a pool; likewise, **you do not want your first experience with TRICARE to be in the midst of a critical illness or injury.** It is far better to start with small steps so that you will be ready for greater challenges when they inevitably occur. This means filing simple claims for smaller things at first, to perfect your skills before larger issues arise. Train yourself so that you will be ready for whatever the future brings.

I run a number of Facebook groups focused on using TRICARE around the world. In these groups, we interact daily with thousands of beneficiaries. Some of their stories are very uplifting; others are wrenching. Quite routinely we encounter a frantic post that goes something like this:

> *"Help! I'm a newcomer here. We live in (Spain, Korea, Belize, etc.). We just found out my (wife, husband, child) has (cancer, stroke, concussion) and we don't know what to do. Do we need to go to a military hospital? Will TRICARE pay? How do we find an approved doctor? We're in a panic and don't know what to do!"*

This semi-fictitious post is an aggregation of actual cries for help in our forum. Can you imagine a loved one suddenly becoming sick or injured in a country where you may not speak the language, don't understand the health system, and are unsure what your health plan covers or how to use it? What if *you* are the one who is hospitalized, and your spouse must figure

2

this out alone? A survey in our group revealed that nearly 80% of our members have little or no idea of how to proceed in such an emergency. Those results caused me to intensify my efforts to reach and educate more of our military community.

Finding yourself in this type of situation is both tragic and unnecessary. The last thing you want to be doing in the midst of a crisis is clicking on websites, desperately trying to figure out what to do. In that moment, you need to be focused on your loved one, confidently guiding their medical care because you already know what TRICARE will cover and know how to use it. That is the purpose of this book.

Don't let your first experience with TRICARE be in the middle of a crisis. There is too much at stake and no need for problems if you will take steps to prepare. The lesson from this is: **Learn to use TRICARE <u>now</u>. Practice it. It is a skill that can be intentionally learned**, just like swimming, baking a cake, or riding a bike. Then, when the need arises, you will be ready. Let's start at the beginning.

What is TRICARE?

Here are some basic definitions to help us get started:

Sponsor: A military member, military retiree, or Guard/Reserve member.

Beneficiary: All who are eligible for TRICARE, including sponsors, their spouse, children, or others. Chapter 2 provides a full list of potential beneficiaries.

Military Treatment Facility (MTF): A military hospital or clinic.

TRICARE is a health program within the Military Health System (MHS) that is intended primarily for military members, retirees, medical retirees, certain reservists, and their eligible family members. TRICARE offers comprehensive coverage compliant with the Affordable Care Act (ACA) including preventive/wellness care, mental health care, prescription drugs, and a broad range of diagnostic and treatment services. Beneficiaries can get care either at an MTF or through civilian health care providers. Your circumstances are impacted by:

- **Your status:** Active duty or retired, family member, reservist, or surviving family member of a deceased sponsor
- **Where you live:** Overseas, stateside, near an MTF
- **Which plan you are in:** Prime, Prime Remote, Select, TRICARE for Life, etc.
- **Your age:** Medicare-eligible or not; retired reservist under age 60; adult child of a sponsor
- **Your preferences:** Choice of plan; choice of Primary Care Manager; use of in-network or non-network care
- **Your situation:** Are you facing a health emergency or dealing with something more routine?

One common mistake is to confuse TRICARE with the health benefits offered under the Department of Veterans Affairs (VA). **The VA and TRICARE are entirely separate programs differing in terms of eligibility, medical services, access, and cost.** To contrast VA with TRICARE:

- Most non-retired vets do not qualify for TRICARE, because TRICARE is primarily for active duty and retired members, and their families.
- Military retirees with TRICARE may not qualify for VA health benefits if they have not obtained a VA disability rating or signed up for VA Health Care. Read more about VA Health Care later in this chapter, which is available to many vets even without a service-connected disability.
- CHAMPVA, a VA health program for family members of certain disabled veterans, cannot be used by those who are eligible for TRICARE.

4

The rules for using TRICARE, whether in the U.S. or abroad, are basically the same everywhere. A notable exception is the Philippines, which has unique rules which are explained in Chapter 8. Despite the consistency of TRICARE rules worldwide, many beneficiaries may find TRICARE more confusing or challenging to use overseas. This is not due to any difference in your TRICARE plan, but for a variety of other reasons:

- TRICARE network providers are scarce overseas, which means users must follow the pricing structure of non-network providers and learn to file claims.

- International healthcare providers are less familiar with TRICARE than U.S.-based providers. They may not know how to validate your benefits and coverage, or do not care to make the effort.

- TRICARE users living or traveling overseas are often uncertain about which providers they are allowed to see.

- Healthcare practices vary widely from country to country, which can be baffling to Americans overseas.

- Language or cultural barriers overseas can lead to further obstacles when seeking care outside the U.S.

For these reasons, we often find that TRICARE users who live overseas or are away from home have a greater need for assistance and support than when they are at home in familiar surroundings. We hope to provide that support through this book, our social media groups, and other resources which we will mention later.

Regions, Programs and Contractors

A variety of contractors manage the many TRICARE regions and programs. It is essential to ensure that you are enrolled in the right region with the correct contractor to get the most from your benefits. Your regional contractor can verify that you are in the right plan. The different contractors and programs are:

TRICARE Around the World

- **TRICARE East**
  - Humana Military
  - www.tricare-east.com

- **TRICARE West**
  - HealthNet
  - www.tricare-west.com

- **TRICARE Overseas**
  - International SOS (ISOS)
  - www.tricare-overseas.com

- **TRICARE for Life (TFL)**
  - Wisconsin Physician Services (WPS)
  - www.tricare4u.com

- **U.S. Family Health Plan (USFHP)**
  - Various providers listed at www.usfhp.com

- **Active Duty Dental Program (ADDP)/ TRICARE Dental Program (TDP)**
  - United Concordia
  - secure.addp-ucci.com

- **FEDVIP Vision and Dental Plans**
  - Optional fee-based vision and dental care for retirees, reservists, and eligible family members.
  - Run by the Office of Personnel Management (OPM).
  - Approved contractors offer a variety of vision and dental plans; each sets their own price.
  - www.benefeds.com

In managing your health benefits online, use the website of your regional contractor: TRICARE East, West, Overseas, or TRICARE for Life. You will create accounts on the contractor's site to submit and track claims and communicate about your benefits. The **tricare.mil** website has a great deal of useful information, but **you will not have an account there, nor manage your care there.** While people speak generically about "calling TRICARE", the reality is that most of the time you will be dealing with TRICARE regional contractors.

Enroll in the region in which you spend the most time. For instance, if you spend eight months of the year in Germany and four months in the U.S., you should enroll with TRICARE Overseas. **You do not need to switch plans or regions as you travel back-and-forth.** Retirees who spend substantial time abroad will find it advantageous to be in TRICARE Select, not in a stateside Prime plan, for reasons that will be explained later.

<u>All</u> **members get full TRICARE benefits at home and urgent or emergency care worldwide.** With non-managed care plans like TRICARE Select and TRICARE for Life, all benefits are easily used worldwide, including routine (non-emergency) care. This makes it quite easy to travel with TRICARE, once you understand how this works.

TRICARE divides the world into three regions: East, West, and Overseas.

TRICARE East covers the eastern U.S., including Alabama, Arkansas, Connecticut, Delaware, Florida, Georgia, Illinois, Indiana, Iowa (Rock Island Arsenal area only), Kentucky, Louisiana, Maine, Maryland, Massachusetts, Michigan, Mississippi, Missouri (St. Louis area only), New Hampshire, New Jersey, New York, Ohio, North Carolina, Pennsylvania, Oklahoma, South Carolina, Rhode Island, Tennessee, Texas (excluding El Paso area), Vermont, Virginia, Washington DC, West Virginia, and Wisconsin.

TRICARE West covers the western U.S., including Alaska, Arizona, California, Colorado, Hawaii, Idaho, Iowa (excluding Rock Island Arsenal area), Kansas, Minnesota, Missouri (excluding St. Louis area), Montana, Nebraska, Nevada, New Mexico, North Dakota, Oregon, South Dakota, Texas (El Paso area only), Utah, Washington, and Wyoming.

TRICARE Around the World

TRICARE Overseas includes U.S. territories and all international locations.

When you become eligible for Medicare (age 65, for most people), **you <u>must</u> enroll in TRICARE for Life (TFL) to maintain your TRICARE benefits, even if you live overseas.** Enrollment is done by signing up for Medicare Parts A and B. Part A is free, but there is a fee for Part B. There are exceptions to this rule, which are explained in Chapter 6.

While TRICARE plans provide the care you need wherever you go, **TRICARE Plus** and **Direct Care Only (DCO)** can be used only in Military Treatment Facilities (MTF) under limited conditions. TRICARE Plus and DCO do <u>not</u> pay for services by civilian providers. Learn more about these in Chapter 6.

2018 Program Realignment

TRICARE was realigned in January 2018 in response to MHS guidance and Congressional legislation. Several major changes occurred at that time:

- The U.S. was reorganized from three regions into two: TRICARE East and West.
- New contractors were brought on board to run each of these regions and programs.
- TRICARE Standard and Extra, widely used plans before 2018, were discontinued.
- New plans were introduced including TRICARE Prime, Select, and Plus. These are explained in Chapter 6.
- A two-tiered pricing system was introduced, based on the sponsor's initial date of military service. Older members, referred to as Group A, were placed into the existing price structure. Newer members, Group B, have a different pricing model. This is explained in the next section.

During the 2018 realignment, outreach was conducted to enroll beneficiaries in one of the new plans. Some users failed to enroll and were shifted to a status of "Direct Care Only" (DCO). **DCO is a highly restrictive status, <u>not</u> a TRICARE plan, and severely limits your access to care.** Under DCO, you can obtain care <u>only</u> at an MTF on a space-available basis. It does <u>not</u> cover care by civilian providers. This change in status can make it difficult or impossible to get the care you need.

If you have not used TRICARE since the 2018 realignment, you might be in DCO status without even knowing it. If you are unsure, it is imperative that you call your regional contractor to check. Direct Care Only is discussed more thoroughly in Chapter 6.

In 2018, **the TRICARE Retiree Dental Program ended**, and retirees were offered optional dental coverage under FEDVIP. See Chapter 4 for details of dental programs.

Group A vs Group B

One of the changes introduced in 2018 is a two-tiered pricing structure. Members will fall into one of two groups.

- **Group A** consists of members whose initial date of service is prior to January 1, 2018. These members and their dependents were grandfathered into an earlier price structure.

- **Group B** consists of members and their dependents whose initial military service is on or after January 1, 2018. Other than active duty service members – for whom care is nearly always free – Group B members follow a newer pricing structure.

You will need to know which group you are in when reading about costs in Chapter 7. Call your regional contractor if you are unsure.

2021 Changes to TRICARE Select

On January 1, 2021, a **new enrollment fee** was initiated for many Group A retirees in TRICARE Select. Sponsors who are medically retired and their family members and survivors are exempt.

During the Open Season enrollment period in the fall of 2020, affected members were required to arrange for payment of this new fee. **Any enrollees who failed to do this were eventually <u>disenrolled</u> from their TRICARE Select plan** and placed into a status of Direct Care Only (DCO. This provides minimal access to care and, for some members, no access at all. You do NOT want to be in a DCO status.

If you are a Group A retiree in Select and do not recall arranging for payment of this fee, or have not used TRICARE since early 2021, **it is possible that you are no longer enrolled in a TRICARE plan.** Call your regional contractor to determine your status and see what alternatives are available to restore benefits for yourself and your family members.

VA Health Care

While this book is not intended to cover VA disability benefits, there is one aspect of VA that is worthy of a deep dive: **There is another path to getting care at the VA that does NOT require any service-connected disability.**

Whenever I talk about this online, the message is widely misunderstood or disbelieved. Many are unable to let go of what they think they know about the VA, insisting that you <u>must</u> have a disability rating in order to get health services at the VA. I, too, was doubtful, but gave it a try and found that I was able to easily apply online. A few weeks later, I began receiving care from the VA and was even provided hearing aids – all without a service-connected disability!

Imagine that there are two ways into the VA:

- The traditional path, known as **VA Disability**, is for vets with a service-connected disability.

- A lesser-known route, called **VA Health Care**, is for vets who qualify based on service history or financial status <u>without</u> any service-connected disability.

With VA Health Care, a great many vets are eligible for benefits and **can apply in just minutes!** There is no review of your military medical record, no panel of doctors assessing your claim, no long sessions with Veteran Service Organizations, no qualifying medical exam, and no drawn-out litigation. For those who already receive VA disability benefits, acceptance into VA Health Care can expand their health care options, offering a full range of care beyond that provided for the disability.

VA Health Care can be used <u>only</u> within the United States and U.S. territories. It cannot be used internationally, and it is not part of the VA Foreign Medical Program (FMP).

Within the U.S., it may be 100% free, depending on the veteran's income, assets, disability rating, and other factors. Copayments, if any, range from $15 for a prescription refill or primary care visit to $50 for specialty care, such as a hearing test or CT scan. Get full details at **www.va.gov/health-care**.

Based on information that you provide during the application process, the VA will conduct a **Geographic Means Test**. This assesses your income based on your ZIP Code and number of dependents. If you fall below the income limit for your location, you are eligible to enroll in VA Health Care if **all** of the following are true:

- You served in the active military (including activation in the National Guard or Reserves by a federal order), **and**

- You were not dishonorably discharged, **and**

TRICARE Around the World
- You meet at least one of the following service requirements for enrollment (see below).

You must meet **at least <u>one</u>** of these service requirements:
- You served before September 7, 1980, **or**
- You served at least 24 consecutive months or for your full active-duty period, **or**
- You were discharged for a hardship (early out), **or**
- You were discharged for a service-connected disability.

Time spent on active-duty status for training does not count toward the service requirements.

To apply, fill out VA Form 10-10EZ, which can be done online at **www.va.gov/health-care/apply/application**. If approved, you will get a phone call to complete your enrollment and assign you to a VA primary care doctor. After the telephone interview, you will meet with your VA doctor, either in-person or remotely via a video chat. You can call 1-877-222-VETS (8387) to discuss your eligibility.

Your VA doctor will review your medical history, determine if any specialty appointments are needed, and input your current prescriptions into the VA system. **Even with VA Health Care, you will retain all of your TRICARE benefits** and can use either one for any given claim.

See my real life story in Chapter 4 about obtaining hearing aids at no cost through VA Health Care – with no service-connected hearing loss! For me, this was a savings of over $4,000. If you already receive disability care at the VA, enrollment in VA Health Care can provide you with an even wider range of medical care.

VA Priority Groups

The VA Health Care program uses priority groups to allocate care to veterans. Your priority group determines what care you may be eligible for and your co-payment, if any. This is not the same as VA rating, which allocates disability benefits solely on the basis of service-connected disabilities. There are eight priority groups: Priority Group 1 gives the highest precedence for care and no copayments. Priority Groups 6-8 have lower precedence and charges copayments for most types of care. See **www.va.gov/health-care/eligibility/priority-groups**.

Priority groups consider a number of factors, including:

- Your military service history
- Your disability rating
- Your income and assets
- Whether or not you qualify for Medicaid
- Other benefits you may be receiving, such as VA pension

You are assigned your priority group during the application process based on the information that you provide. Veterans with low income or service-connected disabilities are assigned higher precedence (a lower-number group). Those with higher income and no service-connected disabilities are assigned lesser precedence (a higher-number group). If your local VA hospital or clinic has limited capacity to serve the veteran community, then those with higher precedence would be seen first.

VA Disability Benefits

VA Disability Benefits are the more "traditional" side of VA. To qualify for care, you must obtain a VA rating for a service-connected disability, which can be a time-consuming and complicated task.

Depending on your rating, you may be entitled to specific, defined care by the VA plus disability pay and other benefits. This book and our social media groups do not cover VA disability benefits in-depth. **For further information, visit VA.gov** or contact a veteran's group such as VFW (Veterans of Foreign

Wars) or DAV (Disabled American Veterans). Their contact information can be found in Chapter 12.

Overseas, the VA offers care for service-connected disabilities through the **Foreign Medical Program (FMP).** This program allows eligible veterans to see civilian providers around the world, pay out-of-pocket, and submit a claim for reimbursement. You may find providers overseas who will bill directly to VA, so you would have <u>no</u> out-of-pocket expenses. **You must <u>pre-register</u> to use FMP, so enroll <u>before</u> the need arises.** The approval process may take some time, so start early. Visit **www.va.gov/communitycare/programs/veterans/fmp/ index.asp** for more information.

There is one VA clinic outside the U.S., an outpatient clinic in Manila for service-connected disabilities only. To learn more about veteran benefits in the Philippines, visit **benefits.va.gov/persona/veteran-abroad-philippines.asp**.

Another option is to receive VA-funded care from civilian providers within the United States and U.S. territories through **Community Care**. This can be used when the needed care is not available within the local VA system. **Pre-approval is required** from the VA facility. Learn more about Community Care at **www.va.gov/communitycare**.

Those living internationally who have both FMP and TRICARE must choose which one to use for any given claim. There are good arguments on both sides.

- With TRICARE, you will have a copayment. You normally pay upfront but can get your money back in a few weeks once you learn how to prepare high-quality TRICARE claims. Your money can be refunded by direct deposit to a U.S. bank account.

- With FMP, your expenses will be fully reimbursed, but it can take up to a year. FMP does not offer direct deposit; they will mail a check. This can be problematic overseas either due to unreliability of the mail or the challenge of depositing a check in U.S. dollars to a foreign bank account.

- In both cases, you might find hospitals or clinics who will bill directly to TRICARE or to FMP. This can reduce your cash outlay when getting care and avoid the need for submitting a claim.

Veterans living in the U.S. who are rated with Permanent and Total Disability (P&T) are eligible for full health care through VA, not just for service-connected issues. This is not true with FMP, however. FMP covers only the rated disability and anything known to be aggravating such conditions. The dependents of these veterans also may receive health benefits through the Civilian Health and Medical Program of the Department of Veterans Affairs (CHAMPVA). However, **dependents who are eligible for TRICARE cannot enroll in CHAMPVA**, even if they have not enrolled in TRICARE.

For more information on VA benefits, visit **www.va.gov**. Refer to Chapter 12 for local and online resources.

TRICARE vs Commercial Insurance

A frequent question in our online forums is this: *If I have TRICARE, do I need to purchase additional coverage?*

Whether to buy additional insurance is a deeply personal decision that only you and your spouse can make. It goes beyond mere financial considerations. Some people lack confidence that TRICARE coverage will be there when they need it, or they find it too confusing. I find this viewpoint unfortunate, needlessly costing members thousands of dollars each year.

In our Facebook groups, we have helped many members work through these complex decisions. The question is not whether TRICARE is too hard. The real question is: *Are you*

willing to expend the effort to learn how to use the benefits that you have earned through your service and sacrifice? My perspective is that TRICARE is not hard to use; it is only hard to <u>learn</u> to use because, until now, there has been no comprehensive training. With the right learning tools, TRICARE is actually quite simple.

A financial comparison to an employer-provided plan might look something like this. These examples are generalizations of real-world figures but do not reflect any single actual policy.

Annual premium
- TRICARE: $0-$6,000 per person (average $600 per family)
- Commercial policy: $4,000-$10,000 per person

Annual deductible
- TRICARE: $0-$700 per family
- Commercial policy: $2,000-$10,000 per family

Annual out-of-pocket expenses
- TRICARE: $3,000-$3,700 maximum per family
- Commercial policy: Unlimited; no cap on expenses

Crunching the numbers, a family may realistically save $10,000 per year or more simply by rejecting employer-provided health coverage and using their TRICARE plan instead. Doing this consistently for 20 years equates to $200,000 in cost savings. Investing the saved money can significantly boost your nest egg and enhance your retirement.

If you have other comprehensive health coverage, such as an employer-sponsored plan, national health care in another country, or travel medical insurance, that policy is known as Other Health Insurance (OHI). When you have OHI, TRICARE becomes "second payer", and you must file a claim with the OHI first. This is a matter of federal law and is taken quite seriously by TRICARE. Once your OHI claim is settled and paid out, you can submit a TRICARE claim for any remaining unpaid amounts.

This matter of first payer/second payer is a big reason why I have never purchased any other insurance for my family. It's bad enough dealing with one insurer; why would I want to deal with two? I don't relish the thought of having to submit claims to two different policies every time I see a doctor. I know that TRICARE will take care of my family – and it always has – so I have never felt the need to have any additional insurance.

Expert tip: In job negotiations, look carefully at the employer's health plan. You may find that TRICARE offers superior coverage at lower cost. You can decline the employer's plan and avoid payroll deductions for health care: more money saved!

Public Law 109-364, Section 707 prohibits employers from providing incentives to TRICARE-eligible employees to decline the company health plan. You are free to decline your employer's health plan on your own, but do not use this as a bargaining chip for higher salary.

Travel Insurance

Choosing to buy travel medical insurance is a somewhat different calculation. This is insurance that covers medical expenses while on travel internationally. These policies are sometimes referred to as "travel insurance" but that term can also encompass such expenses as lost luggage, missed flights, or canceled reservations. For the purpose of this discussion, we use both terms to mean medical coverage for international travelers.

All TRICARE plans cover urgent and emergency care worldwide. Additionally, while you are traveling, non-Prime plans like Select will cover even routine care without the need for a referral. Despite this, many people are uncomfortable relying on TRICARE while traveling either due of their lack of familiarity with TRICARE or because they might have to pay medical bills up front and then file a claim for reimbursement. If you don't have ready access to cash or adequate credit card limits, this can be a concern. Also bear in mind that in some parts of the world, hospitals do not accept credit cards. They may be cash-only, adding to the complexity of your decision.

This question of whether travel insurance is needed for international travel is the reason that I started my Facebook group in the first place. Time after time, I was seeing military members and retirees tell each other that TRICARE cannot be used overseas, and that members should purchase commercial travel insurance. Try as I might, I was unable to convince people otherwise, so I started the Facebook group *"TRICARE Around the World"* to help educate the military community. This book is an outgrowth of that effort.

A big advantage of commercial policies is that leading insurers will work directly with foreign hospitals to arrange for bill payment, alleviating the need to come up with cash if you are hospitalized overseas. **Even some credit cards provide this coverage,** particularly if you paid for your travel expenses on that card. Contact your card issuer to ask.

Short-term travel medical insurance can be obtained very affordably, and many TRICARE users do this for peace of mind. Personally, I have never purchased travel insurance. I am confident that TRICARE will provide the protection I need, although I realize not everyone agrees with that approach.

Many commercial travel policies also cover medical evacuation: transportation back to the U.S. if you require extended medical treatment or recuperation. Without evacuation coverage, medical transportation can be prohibitively expensive for critically sick or injured patients. TRICARE plans include limited provisions for air evacuation only in cases of medical necessity. You are at the mercy of TRICARE to determine if your case qualifies or not. TRICARE coverage for air ambulance/ medical evacuation is discussed in Chapter 4.

TRICARE Supplements

Some TRICARE beneficiaries choose to purchase a TRICARE supplement policy. A supplement covers TRICARE deductibles and copayments and is <u>not</u> considered to be first payer or OHI. With a supplement, your TRICARE plan is still first payer.

Just like buying other commercial health insurance, this is a highly personal decision. Our view is that most families will not need a supplement, particularly active duty families for whom the TRICARE annual cap is quite low. When you do the analysis, really what you are insuring against is the amount of copayment you would pay each year. In 2022, a retiree family on TRICARE Select, the maximum copayment is $3,700 - $3,900 (the limit of the catastrophic cap). This is the greatest benefit that you would get from a supplemental policy, and that is only if you max out copayments for the year.

For active duty families, the cap is much lower: around $1,000 – $1,200 per year. This makes the argument against buying a supplemental policy even stronger.

We can see only one case where it would make sense to buy a supplement: for a retiree family with recurring, predictable medical expenses that reach the catastrophic cap each year. If your family has predictably high medical costs due to a chronic condition, then it might make sense to purchase a TRICARE supplement.

You can find an excellent checklist of the questions that you should ask when shopping for a supplemental policy at **www.tricare.mil/Plans/OHI/SuppInsurance**.

Immigration and Visa Issues

Many nations around the world require travelers to obtain health insurance as a condition of entry. This trend accelerated during the COVID-19 pandemic. Each nation specifies their own minimum level of coverage including coverage for treatment of coronavirus. A letter from the insurance provider detailing this coverage may be required for entry or to be issued a visa.

TRICARE plans do not have a ceiling on benefits payable, but MHS has long resisted stating this in a letter. As a result, TRICARE plans are not accepted by many countries as proof of coverage, forcing users to purchase commercial insurance simply to meet the entry requirements of a given nation.

For a vacationer, this might be just a mild annoyance; the cost for a few weeks of coverage is minimal. But for expats living abroad, this may result in life-changing travel restrictions. Because some nations will not issue commercial coverage after a certain age, American retirees living abroad may be unable to re-enter their host nation if they step outside the borders.

Thailand, for example, requires travelers to buy from an approved list of Thai insurers, but policies are not sold to anyone over age 70. Since TRICARE will not issue a suitable letter, many retirees in Thailand are unable to obtain the required proof of coverage and they become essentially "trapped" in the country. If they leave, they would not be allowed to return. Those with a home or extended family in their adopted country may be forced to choose between staying there forever or leaving with no hope of returning. All of this could be alleviated by a sentence or two in a letter from MHS attesting to the coverage under their TRICARE plan.

I try to be apolitical in this book, but I find this level of bureaucratic indifference to be a slap in the face to our veterans who have served their nation with valor and distinction. While there might be legal or regulatory matters involved, our view is that a team of skilled government lawyers should be clever enough to craft a letter that would be acceptable to foreign immigration authorities, while still protecting the interests of the U.S. government. We would like to see them take these concerns seriously. The problem could be quickly resolved if there were the organizational will to address it.

We are starting to see some success in this area. Expats in Thailand and the Philippines recently have obtained letters documenting their TRICARE coverage and have used this to re-enter these countries. I will not share the contact information here to obtain these letters since contact information is subject to change, and it is discourteous to publish an individual's contact information without permission. If you would like to learn how others have obtained a tailored letter of TRICARE coverage for visa or immigration purposes, please join our Facebook group *"TRICARE Around the World"* and we can discuss recent developments.

TRICARE and Medicare

At age 65, most people in the U.S. and U.S. territories become eligible for Medicare. Medicare enrollment places TRICARE beneficiaries into TRICARE for Life (TFL). In the U.S., the combination of Medicare plus TFL results in zero cost out of pocket in most cases. TFL covers Medicare deductibles and copays, making your health care potentially cost-free. While you cannot use Medicare internationally, your enrollment ensures that TRICARE remains available to you worldwide. It adds predictability to your health costs and simplifies retirement planning. Whether living in the U.S. or overseas, access to lifetime care at a reasonable cost can be life changing.

This transition to Medicare/TFL can be confusing, and we see a great many questions about this in our social media groups.

- Should I sign up for a Medicare supplement?
- What exactly is Medicare Advantage?
- Why should I pay for Medicare if I live overseas and cannot even use it?

Medicare Advantage and Medicare supplements are two different things. TRICARE beneficiaries should NOT buy a Medicare supplement for reasons explained below. However, they might choose to enroll in an Advantage plan if their personal circumstances so dictate.

A Medicare supplement covers expenses not paid by Medicare, including the 20 percent Medicare copayment and annual deductible. But this is <u>exactly</u> what TRICARE for Life does for you! TFL is often called a "Medicare wrap-around." Within the U.S. and territories, TFL will pay your Medicare copayment and deductibles – it's like getting a Medicare supplement for <u>free</u>. When you visit a Medicare provider, Medicare pays first; whatever is left over is forwarded to TRICARE for payment. The user will not need to file a claim and will normally end up with zero out-of-pocket costs. There is no need for a supplement; it would just be wasted money.

Medicare Advantage is entirely different. Advantage plans are a <u>replacement</u> for Medicare, offered by commercial third-party insurers. When you sign up for Advantage, you are no longer in "regular" Medicare, and you can only see health care providers in your Advantage network. In other words, your choice of providers will be more limited than regular Medicare. Depending on where you live and your need for certain specialists, this might make it harder to get appointments when you need them.

Because Advantage is a commercial replacement for regular Medicare, your connection with TRICARE will not be quite as seamless. You normally will be asked to pay a 20 percent copayment during your doctor visit and will have to submit a TRICARE claim to that money back. Some doctors might waive the copayment to avoid all the paperwork, but they are entitled to the payment if they so choose. This is something that you should ask about before signing up for any Advantage plan.

On the positive side, Advantage plans may give you certain freebies. They might cover your entire cost of Part B enrollment. They might provide gym membership, free rides to your doctor, and vision or dental care. These are valuable benefits which you might find worth the trade-off of being in a more restricted network of providers.

When considering Medicare Advantage, research it carefully, read reviews, and focus on your specific location to ensure that you will have access to the care you need. Your decision to join is irrevocable for one year. You will not be able to back out for the next 12 months. In our Facebook group, we have members using Advantage and those who do not. Most people seem pleased with their decision either way, so it comes down to individual choice.

The final question addresses those **living overseas where Medicare is unavailable.** Members often ask why they should pay for Medicare when it can't be used overseas. The author's strong recommendation is that – with one exception – TRICARE beneficiaries living abroad should pay for Medicare after age 65 for the following reasons.

- If you do not sign up for Medicare at 65 and join later, you will be penalized with higher monthly fees – *for the rest of your life!* The penalty is a ten percent higher premium <u>for each year that you delay</u>. This gets very expensive the longer you wait.

- You might think that you will never return to the U.S. and thus will never need Medicare – but circumstances can (and often do) change. The last thing you want is to find yourself in the U.S. – one of the most expensive health markets in the world – and <u>not</u> have health coverage. A single medical emergency can wipe out your life savings. This becomes ever more likely as we age. You might feel fine now – many of us are quite fit at 60 or 70 years old – but how about 10 or 20 years from now?

- On the other hand, if you are in Medicare and have TRICARE for Life, any medical care in the States will be covered 100 percent. Overseas, you will have a 25 percent copayment, but even that is limited by your annual catastrophic cap. Your risks are quite low no matter where you live – if you remain in Medicare.

- Perhaps you plan on buying cheap, local health insurance overseas. Those monthly premiums increase with age and may become unaffordable. Some countries do not offer commercial health insurance after a certain age. By then, you may find Medicare/TFL is beyond reach financially because of that penalty after age 65, leaving you with no local insurance, no TRICARE, and no Medicare – an untenable situation.

One exception to signing up for Medicare might be the foreign spouse of a deceased retiree, living overseas. If the spouse has lifetime coverage through their national health care system and does not expect ever to return to the United States, then there might be no benefit in maintaining TRICARE eligibility. We see this among German widows of U.S. military retirees living in Germany, where they enjoy affordable, comprehensive care through the German national health system. If they decline Medicare enrollment and lose their TRICARE coverage, they can rely solely on their public health plan.

TRICARE and Retirement Planning

When I am not writing about TRICARE, my other passion is helping people plan for retirement. We are adherents of the FIRE movement: *Financial Independence, Retire Early*. The core principle of FIRE is living a moderate lifestyle accompanied by low debt and aggressive investing, which leads to rapid accumulation of retirement savings. Followed consistently, this can allow one to comfortably retire at a relatively young age.

While the FIRE methodology encompasses a variety of strategies to achieve these goals, there is one issue that often comes up for which we have no good answer for non-military families: ***What do you do if you want to retire early and have no employer-provided health coverage?*** This nagging problem seems insurmountable to many Americans under age 65 and is often the sole reason that some people continue working even when they are otherwise ready to retire.

Fortunately for readers of this book, you already have a solution! With lifetime health care for you and your spouse, **your TRICARE health plan can free you from the shackles of working longer than you wish.** If you choose to retire from a second career before eligibility for Medicare, you can do so without worrying about health insurance. This single advantage may put early retirement within your reach.

In the previous section, we demonstrated a potential cost savings of $10,000 annually by relying solely on TRICARE coverage instead of buying a commercial plan. With 8% returns (easily achievable in equity-based index funds), this would give you nearly $500,000 in 20 years – not to mention any retirement benefits from your military and civilian career. For the sake of your financial security, you owe it to yourself and your family to learn how to do this. Invest the savings. Fully embracing your TRICARE benefits can make the difference between early retirement, late retirement, a prosperous retirement, or perhaps no retirement at all.

Expert tip: If you are contemplating moving overseas and plan to claim Social Security in the future, **make sure that you sign up for a MySSA account <u>before</u> leaving the U.S.** MySSA is required to monitor and apply for your retirement benefits, but anti-fraud measures make it difficult or impossible to create an online account while overseas. Learn more about creating a MySSA account at **www.ssa.gov/myaccount.**

Basic Cost Terms

A working knowledge of vocabulary is essential when discussing any health plan. A great deal of confusion arises when someone misuses a term like "deductible" or "copay", which can lead to costly mistakes. Please study these definitions carefully.

Premium: A recurring payment for insurance coverage that is paid monthly, quarterly, or annually. It is risk-based, meaning the insurer calculates how much they must charge to fully cover health expenses for their customers. Premiums vary each year, depending on the estimated cost of covering their beneficiaries.

Example: TRICARE Young Adult (TYA) is a premium-based plan. By law, TYA is not subsidized with tax dollars. Premiums reflect the insurer's actual cost of covering TYA beneficiaries.

Fee: A recurring payment to join an insurance plan. Fee-based plans are government-subsidized, meaning that much of the cost is covered by tax dollars. Fees differ from premiums in that a fee covers only certain administrative costs of the insurer, whereas premiums cover the full cost of providing health care.

Example: TRICARE Select for retirees is fee-based. The cost is relatively affordable since TRICARE Select is financed mostly by tax dollars.

Deductible: The amount that one must pay before insurance benefits kick in. It is calculated on an annual basis and resets to zero at the start of each calendar year. Until the deductible is met, beneficiaries pay the full cost of care. Once they reach the deductible amount, however, their insurance starts to cover the cost of care. It is calculated on a "per year" basis, not "per claim."

Example: TRICARE Select for Group A retirees has an annual deductible of $150 per person (maximum of $300 per family). Benefits begin after your submitted claims exceed $150. TRICARE Prime has zero deductible meaning that TRICARE Prime benefits start with the very first dollar spent.

Copayment or copay: A fixed dollar amount, not a percentage, that you pay for a covered service or drug.

Example: There is a $14 copay for generic medications from a retail pharmacy (except for Active Duty members). This flat rate is regardless of the cost of the drug. Since this is a fixed dollar amount, it is called a copay.

Cost-Share: A percentage of the total cost that you pay for a covered service. In TRICARE, the percentage depends on the status of the sponsor, status of the beneficiary, the care that is obtained, and which plan is being used.

Example: Group A retirees in TRICARE Select have a 25 percent cost-share when visiting a non-network provider for most procedures. For a medical bill of $800, the patient is responsible for $200 (once the annual deductible has been covered). Since this is percentage-based, it is called a cost-share.

Catastrophic cap: The most that an individual or family will pay out of pocket in a given calendar year for covered services.

Example: Group A retirees in TRICARE Select have an annual catastrophic cap of $3,706 in 2022. After a family pays this amount in copayments, deductibles and fees, all expenses will be covered 100 percent by TRICARE for the rest of the calendar year. All TRICARE plans have a catastrophic cap except for the Point of Service (POS) option under TRICARE Prime.

The monthly fees for all fee-based plans (TRICARE Select, Prime, etc.) count towards fulfilling the annual catastrophic cap. Monthly premiums for premium-based plans do not.

Allowable charges: The maximum amount TRICARE will pay for a procedure or service. This amount may vary by location, TRICARE plan, and category of beneficiary (active duty vs retiree). This is also known as CHAMPUS Maximum Allowable Charge (CMAC). Any procedure that is not covered by TRICARE, such as acupuncture treatment, is considered "non-allowable" and would not be covered at all.

We rarely see claims denied due to exceeding allowable charges, especially overseas where the cost of health care is often far less than in the United States. Learn more about reimbursement rates at **www.health.mil/Military-Health-Topics/Business-Support/Rates-and-Reimbursement**.

For more TRICARE terms and definitions, visit **https://tricare.mil/Costs/Cost-Terms**.

2
Who is Covered?

MANY POTENTIAL BENEFICIARIES MAY BE UNAWARE of their eligibility for TRICARE coverage. This chapter discusses each category of beneficiary, what plans they are eligible for, and under what circumstances.

The gateway to TRICARE eligibility is registration in **DEERS: The Defense Enrollment Eligibility Reporting System.** DEERS is the database which lists everyone entitled to military benefits: family members, retirees, reservists, survivors, etc. **No one can enroll in TRICARE until they are <u>first</u> registered in DEERS** (although newborns have a temporary loophole; see below). Guidelines on how to register in DEERS can be found at **tricare.mil/requireddocuments**.

The following sections provide details. If you have eligibility questions about your family, contact the DEERS/ID office at any military base or your TRICARE regional contractor.

Eligibility

Broadly speaking, TRICARE is a health care program for:
- Active duty military
- Military retirees and medically retired
- Spouses, former spouses, and surviving spouses, including same-sex spouses.
- National Guard and Reservists
- Active and retired members of Coast Guard, U.S. Public Health Service and the National Oceanic and Atmospheric Administration (NOAA)

- Minor children, newborns, adult children (to age 26), and adult children with disabilities (possible lifetime benefits)
- Adopted children, stepchildren, wards, and children of unmarried parents
- Dependent parents and in-laws (TRICARE Plus only)
- Surviving family members of deceased military sponsors
- Medal of Honor recipients and their family members
- Foreign Force Members in the U.S. on military orders

The remainder of this chapter discusses specific eligibility criteria for these categories of members.

Active Duty Service Members

Active Duty Service Members (ADSM) are covered for medical care in nearly all situations, and they should never incur costs for care. They will be enrolled in TRICARE Prime or Prime Remote, depending upon proximity of the nearest MTF. There are instances where an ADSM might have to pay a bill upfront, such as in a remote location where no MTF or network provider is available, but these expenses will be fully reimbursed after they are submitted to the regional contractor.

In cases where an ADSM receives care <u>outside</u> of a military hospital or clinic, they must notify their PCM at the earliest opportunity in accordance with DoD and Service regulations.

Retirees and Medically Retired

TRICARE is the "health care for life" that many of us were promised when we joined. Coverage is continuous from the day of retirement, but **it is not automatic; you must enroll in a plan.** The same holds true for those who are medically retired. If you hold a retiree ID card, you are eligible for TRICARE coverage, but you must <u>enroll in a plan</u>.

It is important to note that **enrolling the retiree into a TRICARE plan does NOT enroll the family members.**

You also need to enroll your family members one by one. This is a common misunderstanding of new retirees, potentially resulting in great hardship the first time a family member seeks care and finds out that they are not in a plan.

The mechanics of shifting from your active duty plan to a retiree plan can be complicated. You first must ensure that DEERS is updated to reflect the sponsor's retiree status, and this can only be done when your separating command has submitted the required paperwork. Some personnel offices are not as diligent as others, and this may not be complete by your final day of active service.

Once DEERS reflects your status as a retiree, you can obtain retiree ID cards for all family members holding a card. Only then can you call the TRICARE regional contractor to enroll in a plan as a retiree. This sequence of events may take a few weeks, but do not fear – you have 90 days from your retirement date to complete this. Any medical expenses incurred during those 90 days will be honored. If you miss the 90-day deadline, contact your regional contractor to request a retroactive enrollment. They will backdate enrollment to your retirement date, but you will have to pay any premiums or fees that you missed. All of this takes careful management to ensure that your benefits don't lapse.

If you retire from the reserves but are not yet drawing retired pay (the so-called "gray area retiree"), you may enroll in TRICARE Retired Reserve until age 60. At age 60, you may transition to TRICARE Prime or Select, which have much more favorable pricing.

At age 65, <u>all</u> retirees transition to TRICARE for Life (TFL). This requires enrollment in Medicare. Even if you live overseas where Medicare cannot be used, you MUST be in Medicare if you want TRICARE benefits to continue after age 65. There are some limited exceptions to this rule, which can be found in Chapter 6 under "TRICARE for Life."

Spouse

The spouse of a TRICARE sponsor is <u>always</u> eligible for TRICARE benefits. Even if legally separated, the spouse remains eligible until divorce or annulment is finalized and sometimes even beyond that. Read the section below about former spouses, if applicable.

Coverage for same-sex spouses became law on June 26, 2013, starting with the date that the sponsor's spouse is registered in DEERS.

There is no requirement for spouses to be in the same TRICARE plan as their sponsor. Each can choose a plan according to their preferences. While an active duty sponsor must be in a managed care plan (e.g., TRICARE Prime or Prime Remote), there is no such requirement for the spouse. Run the TRICARE Plan Finder Tool at **tricare.mil** to find all the plan options for spouses.

Newborns

The newborn of a TRICARE sponsor is automatically enrolled into TRICARE at birth. **Those born stateside** in a Prime Service Area (PSA) will be auto-enrolled into Prime. All others (overseas and non-PSA residents) will be placed into Select. From the enrollment date, you have 90 days to change plans, if desired.

For a child born overseas, you will need a Consular Report of Birth Abroad (CRBA, Form FS-240) to enter your child into DEERS. This document certifies that your child acquired U.S. citizenship at birth. The American Citizen Services (ACS) unit of the nearest embassy will be able to help.

The child's automatic enrollment is temporary. You must register your child in DEERS to maintain ongoing care. You have 90 days in the U.S. or 120 days overseas to enroll your newborn in DEERS. The child does not need a Social Security number (SSN), but their DEERS information should be updated once they do have an SSN.

Any claims for care after that cutoff will be denied if your newborn is not in DEERS. If you miss the enrollment deadline, your child will be placed into a status of Direct Care Only (DCO) until the next enrollment period in November the following year when you must contact your regional contractor to change your child's plan.

DCO provides very limited access to care and should be avoided at all costs. See Chapter 6 to learn more about it. If you have any unpaid claims due to missing the DEERS deadline, you will have a chance to have these claims honored retroactively after your child is in DEERS.

Tips for enrolling newborns into TRICARE can be found at **www.tricare.mil/LifeEvents/Baby/GettingTRICAREforChild**.

Minor Children

Unmarried biological children, stepchildren, and adopted children of sponsors are eligible for TRICARE until age 21 (or age 23 if enrolled full-time in an accredited college leading to an associate degree or higher). Beyond that, eligible unmarried adult children can enroll in TRICARE Young Adult until age 26. (See the following section on Adult Children.)

Other provisions for children include:
- **Unadopted stepchildren** are eligible for TRICARE benefits only if the parent of the child is married to the sponsor. If the marriage ends in divorce, stepchildren lose eligibility on the date the divorce decree is final.
- If the sponsor **adopts his or her stepchildren**, they remain covered even if the marriage ends in divorce.

- **Adult children of TRICARE sponsors who have a serious disability that began prior to age 21** remain eligible for the duration of the disability. See the section below on Adult Children with Disabilities.

- **Children whose sponsor died while serving on active duty** remain eligible for TRICARE until they lose eligibility due to age, marriage, or other reason. See the section below about survivors of deceased sponsors.

In other scenarios, children also may be eligible for TRICARE:

- If born out of wedlock.
- When placed in the custody of a sponsor, either by a court or recognized agency, as a ward, or in anticipation of legal adoption.

In each case, there are amplifying rules and conditions. Contact your regional contractor to learn if your child qualifies. The prerequisite for any beneficiary is to enroll them in DEERS. If you are near a military base, the DEERS/ID office will be able to help. In some countries, you might be able to find a DEERS office associated with the U.S. embassy or at the Joint U.S. Military Advisory Group (JUSMAG), normally affiliated with the embassy.

Adult Children

Adult children age out of your TRICARE plan at age 21 (or at 23 if they are enrolled full time in college). If you are claiming the extension to age 23, you will need a letter from the school's registrar office confirming your child's enrollment each year. Following the age-cutoff, adult children under age 26 may be eligible for TRICARE Young Adult (TYA). The child must be unmarried and must not have access to their own employer-sponsored health plan. TYA has two variants: **TYA-Prime** and **TYA-Select**. These plans are described in Chapter 6.

TYA is a premium-based plan: it is not subsidized with tax dollars, so the cost is higher than plans like Prime and Select that receive tax-funded subsidies. Despite that, TYA may be the most affordable health care option for your adult child. To learn more, visit **tricare.mil/Plans/HealthPlans/TYA**.

Adult Children with Disabilities

Incapacitated or significantly disabled adult children of sponsors may be eligible for continued TRICARE health benefits if they meet the following criteria:

- Incapable of providing their own support
- Dependent on the sponsor for over 50 percent of their support. If the sponsor is deceased, the child must have received over 50 percent of his or her support from the sponsor at the time of death.
- Incapacitation must have occurred prior to age 21 (or age 23 if enrolled as a full-time student).
- Unmarried. If the child marries and the marriage terminates due to divorce, annulment, or death of the spouse, the sponsor may apply for reinstatement of the child's benefits if they continue to meet all other requirements.

The application and approval process can be prolonged. Start well before the 21st birthday to avoid a break in coverage or disqualification due to aging out of their existing plan. Apply for a determination with the following documentation:

- Dependency Statement — Incapacitated Child Over Age 21 (DD Form 137-5)
- Application for Identification Card/DEERS Enrollment (DD Form 1172-2)
- Current physician's statement dated within 90 days. (Contact the sponsor's service representative for details.)

TRICARE Around the World

- If the child is eligible for Medicare Part A, proof of Medicare Part A and Part B enrollment must be provided unless the sponsor is on active duty. If not eligible for Part A, submit a statement from SSA certifying this non-eligibility.
- Birth certificate, if not enrolled in DEERS. If adding a stepchild to DEERS, the parents' marriage certificate is also required.

TRICARE benefits may continue as long as the condition persists. A brief mention of this benefit can be found at **www.tricare.mil/LifeEvents/ChildAdult**.

You can find additional resources for family members with special needs at: **www.militaryonesource.mil/family-relationships/special-needs/**

Guard and Reserve Members

TRICARE eligibility for National Guard, Reservists, and their family members varies depending on several factors. **Always use the Plan Finder Tool separately** for the sponsor and for each family member to determine which plans apply to each person. Go to **tricare.mil/Plans/PlanFinder**.

A National Guard or Reserve member who has been activated for more than 30 days on **Federal orders** may be eligible for the same TRICARE plans as active duty members, including their dependents. If activated on **State orders**, there is no TRICARE eligibility.

Under age 60, retired Reserve members may qualify to purchase **TRICARE Retired Reserve,** a premium-based plan. This includes family members and survivors of deceased sponsors if the sponsor was covered by TRICARE Retired Reserve when he or she died. See Chapter 6 for more information or visit **tricare.mil/Plans/HealthPlans/TRR**.

Members of the **Selected Reserve** may be eligible for **TRICARE Reserve Select (TRS)** if they are not on active duty orders and are not covered by the Transitional Assistance Management Program (TAMP) or Federal Employees Health Benefits (FEHB). See Chapter 6 to learn more about TRICARE Reserve Select or visit **tricare.mil/Plans/HealthPlans/TRS**.

At age 60, retired Reserve members and dependents become eligible for the same TRICARE plans as regular retired service members. This includes TRICARE Prime, TRICARE Select, and U.S. Family Health Plan (USFHP).

At age 65, retired Reserve members become eligible for **TRICARE for Life**. They will need to enroll and pay for Medicare to continue their TRICARE coverage. Their dependent family members under age 65 will continue on their other plans until they, too, reach age 65.

Members of the **Individual Ready Reserve** are not eligible for any TRICARE coverage.

Survivors of Deceased Sponsors

Surviving family members of deceased sponsors can retain their TRICARE benefits depending upon the sponsor's military status when they passed. Spouses lose eligibility when they remarry and do not regain coverage if that subsequent marriage terminates. Eligibility rules for surviving family members are summarized in the paragraphs below; full details can be found at **tricare.mil/Plans/Eligibility/Survivors**.

Use the **Plan Finder Tool** to determine suitable plans for a surviving spouse and children. In the first window, **select "Surviving Spouse" or "Surviving Child"** rather than "Spouse" or "Child." When it later asks for sponsor status, select their status at the time of death. Answer all remaining questions to see which plans each family member is eligible for.

The spouse of a sponsor who dies while on active duty is considered a "transitional survivor" for three years from the date of death. The spouse will retain existing health options for three years at the same cost as before unless they remarry.

Surviving children of deceased active duty sponsors will be considered Active Duty Family Members (ADFM) until they age out of the program at age 21 or 23. They are not subject to the three-year transitional period. Their enrollment and other costs will be the same as children of active duty sponsors.

Surviving family members also should explore the Continued Health Care Benefit Program (CHCBP) which can provide transitional coverage when other plans expire. See Chapter 6 for details of this program.

If a sponsor dies after retiring from active duty (either regular or a medical retirement), surviving family members remain eligible for TRICARE with the same plan options and costs as before. The surviving spouse will remain eligible for TRICARE unless they remarry. Children remain eligible until they age out or lose eligibility for TRICARE for other reasons.

Surviving family members may retain **transitional dental coverage under the TRICARE Dental Program Survivor Benefit Plan (TDP).** A surviving spouse can remain on TDP for three years, then transition to FEDVIP dental. Children can remain on TDP until they lose eligibility at age 21 or 23. While on TDP, survivor premiums are covered at no cost. Learn more at: **www.tricare.mil/CoveredServices/Dental/SurvivorBenefit**

Former Spouse

If the former spouse of a military sponsor has not remarried, they may be eligible for continued TRICARE coverage after dissolution of the marriage by divorce or annulment. If the couple is separated but not divorced, the spouse's eligibility continues indefinitely.

The former spouse will be listed in DEERS under their own name and SSN, not that of their former sponsor. TRICARE benefits will be lost if the former spouse remarries or enrolls in an employer-sponsored health plan.

Upon dissolution, there are two rules which govern eligibility of the former spouse.

- **Under the 20/20/20 rule,** the former spouse can keep TRICARE benefits **indefinitely** if: (1) married to the service member for at least 20 years; (2) the service member served in the armed forces for at least 20 years; and (3) the marriage and the period of service overlapped for at least 20 years.

- **Under the 20/20/15 rule,** the former spouse may keep their TRICARE benefits for **one year after the divorce** if: (1) married to the service member for at least 20 years; (2) the service member served in the armed forces for at least 20 years; and (3) the marriage and the period of service overlapped for at least 15 years.

Medal of Honor Recipients & Their Families

Medal of Honor (MoH) recipients and their TRICARE-eligible family members have somewhat expanded access to TRICARE as compared to other members.

- If the MoH recipient has **separated** from the service, then the sponsor and their family members retain the TRICARE benefits of a **retired** sponsor.

- If the sponsor is **retired or on active duty**, then they and their family members will have the same TRICARE benefits as other retired or active duty sponsors.

- If the MoH recipient is **deceased**, surviving eligible family members will retain the TRICARE benefits of survivors of deceased active duty or retired sponsors, depending on whether the sponsor was on active duty or not at the time of death.

See section above on "Survivors of Deceased Sponsors" for further explanation of eligibility.

Dependent Parents

If you have a dependent parent or parent-in-law, they may be eligible for limited TRICARE benefits. "Dependent" means that the sponsor is providing more than half of the parent's living expenses. The parent must be enrolled in DEERS, and evidence of support will be required when applying.

The only plan that a dependent parent can enroll in is TRICARE Plus. This plan can be used only at participating MTFs and provides priority access for Primary Care only. Specialty care within an MTF is not assured, and no coverage is provided off base. Acceptance into Plus at one MTF is not transferable to another location. See Chapter 6 for more information about TRICARE Plus.

3
Selecting & Enrolling in a Plan

DECIDING WHICH PLAN TO ENROLL IN can seem daunting. There are so many unfamiliar concepts: Managed vs unmanaged care. Premiums, deductibles, and copayments. In-network, non-network, PCM, and referrals. Hopefully, the previous chapters have helped to clarify the jargon for you.

In this chapter, we walk through the decision-making process so that you can choose the plan that best meets your needs. As always, our Facebook groups are available to ask questions and interact with a supportive community of TRICARE users.

Step 1: Use the Plan Finder Tool

When deciding on which plan to choose for you and your family, the best place to start is the TRICARE Plan Finder tool. This can be found on the official TRICARE website at **tricare.mil/Plans/PlanFinder**.

If the sponsor is active duty, make sure to run this tool <u>twice</u>: once for the sponsor and again for eligible family members. If your family is geographically separated or you have a child away at college, run it for the location of each family member because you may get different results. **If you are planning ahead for military retirement,** run the tool as though you are already retired to see which plans it will recommend for you in retirement. Put in your retirement ZIP Code, if known, as some results are location-dependent. This can help you prepare for your health care transition in retirement.

TRICARE Around the World

The simplest outcome is when the Plan Finder identifies only one available plan. In that case, you have no choice but to enroll in the plan that is offered. For others, especially non-active duty members, it is quite possible that the tool will identify two or more possible plans. In that case, you will have to dig a bit deeper to see which plan best fits your needs.

Here are some possible outcomes from the Plan Finder tool and how you might respond:

- Active duty members will always be directed to TRICARE Prime or Prime Remote. These are managed-care plans and DoD wants active duty members to be assigned to a Primary Care Manager (PCM) to better enhance military readiness. You will enroll in the designated plan.

- Retirees living in the States and ADFM worldwide may be given a choice of TRICARE Prime (managed care), or TRICARE Select (self-directed care). There may also be an option for the **U.S. Family Health Plan** if it is offered near you. USFHP falls under TRICARE Prime, but there are some subtle differences. Carefully review the USFHP website for your location to help in your decision-making process. If you live far from a military base, you might not have the option of using TRICARE Prime. Chapter 6 describes all the plans.

- Retirees and their family members living overseas cannot enroll in TRICARE Prime.

- Any beneficiary over age 65 will be directed to TRICARE for Life (TFL). Enrollment in Medicare Part B is required, including the monthly payment that goes with it. If you are under 65 and eligible for Medicare due to a qualifying medical condition, you may be given a choice of TFL, Prime or Select. You may lose access to Medicare once the medical condition is alleviated. This has a significant impact on fees because you must pay the cost of Medicare

Part B when on TFL, which is higher than the monthly fee for Prime or Select. For more details, see the section on Tricare for Life in Chapter 6.

- It is quite possible for different family members to be in different plans. The sponsor might be in TRICARE for Life, the spouse in Prime, and their adult child in TRICARE Young Adult. In this case, you will need to become familiar with each of these plans in order to use them effectively.

There is an option called **TRICARE Plus**. The Plan Finder Tool will never recommend Plus except for dependent parents or parents-in-law; this is the only plan in which they may enroll. For other beneficiaries, Plus is an add-on to non-managed care plans such as TRICARE Select or TRICARE for Life. TRICARE Plus offers primary care at participating MTFs, but it does not assure access to specialty care and will not cover any care from civilian providers. **No one should rely on Plus as their sole health plan because it does not provide comprehensive care.** Learn more about this in Chapter 6.

Step 2: Evaluate Your Options

Once you run the Plan Finder Tool, it's time to decide which plan best meets your needs. Should you choose TRICARE Prime, which has higher monthly fees but more generous benefits? Should you choose TRICARE Select, which has a lower monthly fee but higher copay and no PCM?

TRICARE provides two additional tools to help with this decision. These tools allow you to examine plans side-by-side for an easier comparison of costs and benefits:

- The Plan Comparison Tool, which is found at **tricare.mil/Plans/ComparePlans**
- The Cost Comparison Tool, which is found at **tricare.mil/CompareCosts**

When comparing two plans, consider your family's typical usage of health care. Which cost structure appeals to you more and is likely to save you the most money? An even bigger consideration may be this: **Under TRICARE Prime, you are assigned a Primary Care Manager (PCM)** who will be your first stop for most care. Only with their referral can you be seen by a specialist. Many people find comfort in being under the care of a PCM who guides their health care choices.

Under TRICARE Select, you do NOT have a PCM. You make appointments as you see fit and do not need referrals to see a specialist. Many people prefer the freedom of making their own health care choices without the added step of visiting a PCM.

The author has been enrolled in TRICARE Select as a retiree in Japan, Thailand, and Hawaii, and it worked well in each of these locations. We could just pick the specialist we needed and go. There were no network providers in our overseas locations, so we paid up-front and became proficient in the art of filing claims. In Hawaii, we found plenty of network providers and have never had to file a claim here. All in all, we have been very pleased with TRICARE Select everywhere we go.

Know your rights! In January 2022, three military spouses – in Germany, Guam, and Australia – each shared in our Facebook group that they were "forced" into TRICARE Prime against their wishes. All three were told they had to choose Prime, even though each preferred Select.

We believe these members were misinformed. The only ones who <u>must</u> use Prime (or Prime Remote) are active duty military members. All others who are eligible for Prime may enroll in Select if they so choose. Enrollment in Select makes it easier to see the specialist of your choice, which is why many prefer Select over Prime. As of this writing, one of them was able to go back – armed with more information – and force a change to her enrollment. The others are still working on it.

There are no right or wrong answers to your choice of plans. It is not always a matter of dollars and cents. Sometimes, being able to see the doctor of your choice may be more important than deductibles, copayments, or access to your MTF.

Step 3: Take Care of All Family Members

When selecting a TRICARE plan, especially after leaving active duty, it is important to think about each family member. Each person must be individually enrolled; it is not automatic. Some key points to keep in mind:

- **Family members do not have to be in the same plan.** There are many situations in which different members would benefit from being in different plans. Talk this over carefully with your TRICARE regional contractor.

- **Creating an account in your regional web portal is NOT the same as enrolling in a plan.** To enroll your family in a TRICARE plan, call your regional contractor. They can take all your enrollment information by phone.

- **There are only specific times of the year when you may enroll in a plan:** Either during the annual Open Season or when you have a Qualifying Life Event (QLE). If you miss these opportunities, you may have to wait an entire year before you get another chance. See the next section for information about this.

Due to medical privacy laws, TRICARE will not talk to you about your spouse or adult children without pre-authorization. To convey such authorization, create online accounts for each family member and link the accounts in the web portal. **This linking of accounts grants permission** for you to discuss your family member's medical care and enrollment. Appendix A includes instructions for linking accounts and managing family health plans in the regional contractor web portals.

Expert tip: Linkage to a child's account expires on their 18th birthday. If you want to remain involved in the management of your adult child's health care, you can re-establish a link to their account only with their consent after they turn 18.

Open Season and QLEs: When to Sign Up

There are two main opportunities to make changes to your family's TRICARE enrollment: During the annual Open Season and after a Qualifying Life Event (QLE). If you miss those time frames, other ways to change enrollment are described below.

Open Season, sometimes called the **Annual Enrollment Window**, takes place each year from mid-November to mid-December. Check **tricare.mil** or our Facebook group for exact dates each year. During Open Season, all TRICARE beneficiaries can make changes to their enrollment, if desired. This can be done with a phone call to your regional contractor or via their web portal. **Any changes made during Open Season will be effective on January 1st of the following year.** Phone lines can be quite busy during this period, so call as early in the enrollment period as possible.

If you do not need to make changes to your plan, you normally do not have to call or take any action during Open Season. However, this is not always true: An exception came in the fall of 2020 when a new fee was initiated for many retirees enrolled in TRICARE Select. To retain coverage, affected members had to arrange payment for the new fee during the 2020 Open Season even though they were not changing plans. So, while the general rule is that you do not need to call if you are not changing plans, watch out for exceptions to the rule.

The other opportunity to switch TRICARE plans is when anyone in your family has a **Qualifying Life Event (QLE)**. Any change made as the result of a QLE becomes effective as of the date of the event. For example, if you got married on April 1st and notified TRICARE on April 20th, any medical expenses incurred by your new spouse would be covered back to April 1st. You generally have **90 days** from the QLE to notify TRICARE of the change. Failure to do so might mean that you will have to wait for the next Open Season to make the enrollment change.

A complete list of QLEs with examples is shown below. You can learn more about TRICARE Qualifying Life Events at **tricare.mil/LifeEvents**.

- **Change in sponsor status.** Examples: Retiring or separating from active duty; Reserve activation or deactivation.

- **Change in family composition.** Examples: Marriage, divorce, or annulment; birth or adoption of a child; guardianship; death in the family.

- **Moving.** Examples: Relocation to a new TRICARE region; an eligible child moving away to college.

- **Government-directed changes.** Example: A government-directed change of your primary care manager or plan.

- **Change in overseas command sponsorship.** Example: Gaining or losing permission to have family members accompany sponsor during an overseas assignment.

- **Age-related changes.** Examples: Retired Reserve member turning 60; reaching Medicare age at 65; adult child losing eligibility at 21 or 23.

- **Gaining or losing Other Health Insurance (OHI).** Examples: Gaining or losing to employer-sponsored health insurance.

If <u>any</u> member of your family has a QLE, then <u>every</u> member of the family has 90 days to change plans. For example, if the sponsor reaches age 65 and signs up for Medicare/TFL, then <u>all</u> family members are in a QLE and have 90 days to change plans, if desired.

There are two additional opportunities to change your family's TRICARE plans:

- If you want to enroll in a premium-based plan, you can do so at any time. A premium-based plan is one that is not subsidized with tax dollars and members bear the full cost of health care through premiums. This includes TRICARE Young Adult, TRICARE Reserve Select, and TRICARE Retired Reserve.

- You can request to change plans when you have a unique family situation by asking your regional contractor for an **Exception to Policy (ETP)**. A military spouse living in Germany, for example, might want to switch from TRICARE Prime to Select to have a greater choice of prenatal care off base during pregnancy. **Approval of ETP is not assured; submit your request early if this is important to you.**

TRICARE Overseas vs Stateside Plans

In our Facebook groups, some retired members have mentioned living overseas full time while remaining in TRICARE Prime with TRICARE East or West rather than enrolling in TRICARE Overseas Select. They believe that they are deriving greater benefit through this strategy, but we disagree for the reasons below. (This does <u>not</u> apply to vacationers, who should remain enrolled in their stateside plan while traveling abroad.)

- If you are enrolled in TRICARE Overseas Select or TRICARE for Life, you can obtain <u>all</u> care – even for routine matters – without pre-approval. These plans have no Primary Care Manager (PCM), so obtaining care overseas is vastly simpler.

- TRICARE Prime has higher monthly fees than TRICARE Overseas Select. These fees add up, especially if you do not use your benefits very often.

- If you are enrolled in TRICARE Prime stateside and seek routine care overseas, you <u>must</u> have pre-approval or a referral from your doctor in the U.S. The logistics for making this request are complicated, and there is no guarantee that your request will be approved.

- It can be difficult or impossible to find an in-network provider overseas, which means your costs under Prime may be higher than you expect.

- If you obtain routine care with Prime <u>without</u> a referral, you will be charged the Point of Service (POS) rate, which is very costly. Your copay is 50 percent in addition to a deductible of $300 per person. None of the costs under the POS option count towards your annual Catastrophic Cap. Learn more about the Point of Service option in Chapter 6.

- If you are in TRICARE Prime and seek emergency care overseas – which should normally be covered – there is always a chance that the claims adjudicator will decide that your condition was not a true emergency. If this happens, you could be liable for the 50 percent POS copayment and/or a long battle to dispute the claim. If you are enrolled in TRICARE Select, this would not happen because you can seek <u>all</u> types of care under Select without pre-approval, whether it is urgent, emergency, or routine care.

Remaining enrolled in a stateside Prime plan while living overseas potentially introduces problems and risks. It is much better – in the author's opinion – for retiree members living overseas to enroll in an overseas plan.

4
Covered Care

TRICARE PLANS OFFER A BROAD RANGE of health services for beneficiaries. The TRICARE website says: *"TRICARE covers services that are medically necessary and considered proven."* It goes on to explain that *"medically necessary means it is appropriate, reasonable, and adequate for your condition."*

In general, the criteria for approving any claim with TRICARE is:

- Is the care medically necessary?
- Is it appropriate to the disease or condition?
- Is it a proven treatment?

If you can answer yes to all three questions, there's a good chance the procedure is covered, but it is best to confirm this ahead of time. We will show you how this process works.

The Covered Care Search Tool

There are no specific lists on the TRICARE website of what is covered. Instead, you use the Covered Care Search Tool at **tricare.mil/CoveredServices**. Type a word or phrase in the search box and click "Search." This will bring up a list of related healthcare options, with a discussion of how or if they are covered by TRICARE. You also have the option to browse by category on that page.

As an example, type "Smoking" in the "Covered Services" search box, and it will pop up with the term "Smoking Cessation Services." When you select this, it leads to a page of related procedures.

Test, Item or Service	Covered?	Limits	
Lung Cancer Screening	Yes	Must meet specific criteria.	More >
Over-the-Counter Drugs	It depends	Insulin and diabetes supplies, tobacco cessation products and some other select drugs are covered	More >
Smoking Cessation Services	Yes	See Tobacco Cessation Services	More >

In the second column – "Covered?" – there are three possible entries: "Yes", "No", or "It Depends." Click the word "More" in the final column to get details. You will find:

- "Yes" does not always mean Yes.
- "No" does not always mean No.
- "It depends" means that you will need to research the details.

In this example, the chart says "Yes" – lung cancer screening is covered. But when you click "More", you learn that coverage is limited by the age of the patient, extent of tobacco usage, and other health disqualifiers. In reality, lung cancer screening should be labeled: "It depends." This disparity comes up often in the "What's Covered" page.

In the same example, Smoking Cessation Services is marked "Yes", but when you click "More" you find that these services are not available to retirees living overseas. This again demonstrates that "Yes" does not always mean "Yes" for covered services.

If you are unsure whether a procedure is covered, call your TRICARE regional contractor or the MHS Nurse Advice Line. If you are facing an expensive procedure and don't want any misunderstanding about your coverage, **ask your regional contractor for a "Benefits Review."** This is a formalized determination that a procedure you want is covered. **Have**

them send the review to you in writing via their secure messaging portal to document what you were told.

Real Life Story: A member in our Facebook group was facing $89,000 for surgery at a German hospital. She called the TRICARE Overseas regional office in the UK for a benefits review, which determined that the procedure was covered. She went forward with the surgery, confident that her claim would be covered.

Another member in Germany was asked by their hospital for proof that TRICARE would pay for her care before being admitted for treatment. TRICARE Overseas conducted a benefits review and prepared a letter listing medical codes for covered procedures, as well as details of her TRICARE coverage. The hospital accepted this letter as proof of coverage and went forward with the procedure without any further complication. The benefits review process is not just for your peace of mind but can also assure the hospital that your medical expenses will be paid.

What is NOT Covered

After settling the question of what *is* covered, you will find that determining what is *not* covered is more straightforward. TRICARE has posted a list of excluded services at: **tricare.mil/CoveredServices/IsItCovered/Exclusions**.

Review the list below but use this information cautiously. Although it is accurate to the best of our research at the time of publication, the information is subject to change at any time. **For the latest advice, visit the TRICARE website or give them a call.** Remember – just because you don't see something on this list does not mean that it is covered or that it applies to you. As we saw in the previous section, some procedures that are listed as "covered" have exclusions or conditions, so they might be covered only for a certain age group, for active duty members only, or only if you meet certain qualifying health conditions.

TRICARE Around the World

On the Exclusion page noted above, there is a link for each excluded item. Clicking the link will disclose any qualifying limitations, exceptions, or amplifying information.

Excluded Services

Acupuncture & Alternative Treatments
Alterations to Living Space, Elevators or Chair Lifts
Assisted Living Facility, Nursing Home, Retirement Home and Long Term Care
Augmentation Mammoplasty
Autopsy Services
Aversion Therapy
Blood Pressure Monitoring Devices
Charges for Missed Appointments
Computerized Dynamic Posturography
Cosmetic Drugs
Domiciliary Care
Dry Needling
Dynamic Posturography
Elective Psychotherapy & Mind Expansion Psychotherapy
Elective Services or Supplies
Electrolysis
Exercise Equipment, Programs or Gym Membership
Experimental Procedures
Fluoride Preparations
Hair Removal
Homeopathic and Herbal Drugs
Hospitalization for Medical or Surgical Error
LASIK Surgery
Learning Disorders & Dyslexia Treatment
Massage
Medical Care from a Family Member
Multivitamins & Megavitamins
Mycotoxin Testing or Toxic Mold Testing
Naturopathic Care
Neurofeedback

Orthoptics
Paternity Test
Postpartum Stay without a Medical Reason
Private Hospital Rooms
Psychiatric Treatment for Sexual Dysfunction
Psychogenic Surgery
Safety Medical Supplies
Sensory Integration Therapy
Sexual Dysfunction Treatment
Therapeutic Absence from Inpatient Facility
Transcutaneous Electrical Nerve Stimulation (TENS)
Vestibular Rehabilitation
Vision Therapy
Vitamin D Screening
Weight Loss Products

Preventive Care

TRICARE plans offer broad coverage for preventive care. Many preventive services are provided at no cost, meaning no copay and no deductible. One question we see a lot in our online forum – especially from retirees living overseas – is whether annual physicals are covered. As always, the short answer is: "It depends." But first, we must get our terminology straight.

There are physicals, wellness exams, preventive exam, and a newer term called "Health Promotion and Disease Prevention Exam." Each of these are covered under different situations.

- **Physicals** are covered for active duty members, active duty family members if required for overseas duty assignment, and when required for school enrollment. TRICARE does NOT cover sports physicals.

- TRICARE covers annual **Well Woman exams** at no cost. This includes breast exam, pelvic exam, Pap smear, HPV DNA testing, and other screenings when ordered or recommended during the exam.

- All TRICARE plans cover annual **Well-Child Care** at no cost until the 6th birthday. Services provided are listed later in this chapter.

- What used to be called a **Preventive Care Exam** is now a **Health Promotion and Disease Prevention (HP&DP) Exam**. The TRICARE cost tables say there is a copayment for this when using a non-network provider, but numerous retirees living overseas (including myself) have been getting full reimbursement for these exams in recent years, even with non-network providers. The trick is to make it clear in your claim that the exam is strictly for preventive care, not for any clinical treatment.

Expert tip: If submitting a claim for a preventive care exam with TRICARE Select, be careful how you phrase it in on the claim form. Do not write "physical" because this is not covered for most beneficiaries, and it will be denied. Also, do not list any physical ailment in the claim, such as "monitor hypertension." If you say that, the visit is no long preventive; it is clinical, and you will have a copayment. Be sure to write only "Annual Preventive Care Exam" or "Health Promotion and Disease Prevention Exam." In recent years, most members have found that such an exam is reimbursed 100%.

During the course of the exam, it is fine to talk to your doctor about any medical issues you may have – that is the whole reason for the exam, and it will not result in denial of your claim. The doctor should schedule a follow-up appointment to deal with those medical issues at another time.

The following is a list of preventive care services covered by TRICARE. Some items have exclusions or limitations; visit **tricare.mil/HealthWellness/Preventive** for details.

Preventive Care Covered Services

Abdominal Aortic Aneurysm Screening
Blood Pressure Screening
Body Measurement
Breast Exams
Breast Magnetic Resonance Imaging (MRI)
Cancer Screening
Cardiovascular Screening
Cholesterol Testing
Colonoscopy
Echocardiogram
Eye Exams
Health Promotion & Disease Promotion Exams
Hearing Exams
Hepatitis B/C Screening
Human Papillomavirus (HPV) Test & Vaccine
Immunizations (CDC-recommended)
Infectious Disease Screening
Lipid Panel
Mammograms
Parent & Patient Educational Counseling
Pediatric Lead Level Screening
Physicals
Rubella Antibodies
Tobacco Cessation Services
Tuberculosis Screening
Well Woman Exams
Well Child Care

Well-Child Care

Newborn care
History and physical examination
Mental health assessment
Developmental and behavioral appraisal
Height and weight measurement
Head circumference until age 2

TRICARE Around the World

> Eye & vision screening at birth and around 6 months old
> Audiology screening before 1 month old
> Dental Screenings
> Routine immunizations
> Tuberculin test at 12 months again in 2nd year of age
> Hemoglobin/hematocrit testing in each of first two years
> Urinalysis in each of first two years
> Annual blood pressure screening age 3-6
> Blood Lead Testing
> Health guidance and counseling; breast feeding and
>   nutrition counseling
> Routine eye exams age 3-6

Full details of well-child care can be found at:
tricare.mil/CoveredServices/IsItCovered/WellChildCare.
For further information on all preventive care services, visit
tricare.mil/HealthWellness/Preventive/GettingCare.

Pharmacy

TRICARE provides comprehensive prescription drug
coverage. There are a variety of ways to receive prescription
medications.

- **At an MTF at no cost**. Some MTFs no longer serve
  retirees or ADFMs who are not enrolled in primary care
  at their facility. Sadly, this trend is gathering momentum
  as MTFs are subjected to staffing reductions.

- **Home delivery via Express Scripts** (normally a 90-
  day supply). Express Scripts will mail only to addresses in
  the U.S., including APO or FPO overseas. Due to local
  law, **home delivery is not available in Germany,**
  whether by APO or German mailing address.

- **At retail pharmacies.** This is nominally priced for a
  30-day supply, but you may find that non-narcotic
  maintenance medications are provided in 90-day refills.

- **Through the VA.** Many veterans can obtain prescription refills from the VA by mail or in person, even without any service-connected disability. See "VA Health Care" in Chapter 1.

TRICARE doesn't cover over-the-counter (OTC) drugs, except for the following:

- Insulin and diabetic supplies
- Tobacco cessation products covered by the tobacco cessation benefit (stateside only)
- Other OTC drugs and supplies including:
  - Cetirizine tablets
  - Fexofenadine tablets
  - Levonorgestrel (Plan B One-Step Emergency Contraceptive)
  - Loratadine tablets
  - Omeprazole (generic of Prilosec OTC)

With limited exceptions, the above OTC drugs are not covered outside of the U.S. or U.S. Territories.

TRICARE's pharmacy program is managed by Express Scripts. Each family member can create an account on express-scripts.com if they would like to manage their prescriptions online. In the portal, members can search for participating pharmacies, order refills, check prices, set up automatic refills by mail, and see which formularies are covered under your plan.

Another feature of Express Scripts is the **Deployment Prescription Program (DPP)**. This allows deploying service members or TRICARE-eligible contractors and government employees (such as a military spouse or retiree) to receive up to 180 days of prescription medications while on deployment or orders. **Exception**: DPP is not available if you have other health insurance (OHI) with a pharmacy benefit. By law, you must use your other insurance first.

DPP also provides for mail delivery to a deployment military address. Allow 3-4 weeks for the first delivery. To sign up, visit **www.militaryrx.express-scripts.com** and select DPP on the "Benefits" menu at the top.

If you need expensive maintenance drugs, pharmacy coverage may well be one of your greatest TRICARE benefits. **TRICARE plans have an annual cap that limits what you will spend on out-of-pocket costs**. Once you reach your annual cap, any further medical expenses for the entire family are covered 100 percent for the rest of the year.

Chapter 7 provides an overview of pharmacy costs. Chapter 9 lists strategies for obtaining prescription refills while traveling.

Hearing Aids

There are four different ways to obtain hearing aids through TRICARE, the VA, and related programs. Each of these methods is explained below.

- TRICARE will cover the cost of hearing aids for active duty service members and their families if the following hearing loss thresholds are met:
  - **Adults:** At least 40 dB (decibel) loss in one or both ears at 500; 1000; 1500; 2000; 3000; or 4000Hz; or at least 26 dB loss in one or both ears at any three or more of those frequencies; or speech recognition score less than 94%.
  - **Children:** At least 26dB loss in one or both ears when tested at 500; 1000; 2000; 3000; or 4000Hz.

  For full details about TRICARE hearing aids, visit **tricare.mil/CoveredServices** and type "hearing aids" in the search box. If you are on TRICARE Prime, get a referral from your PCM to ensure that you are covered.

- Through the Retiree At-Cost Hearing Aid Program (RACHAP) or Retiree Hearing Aid Purchase Program (RHAPP), veteran retirees (but not their family members) may be able to obtain hearing aids at greatly reduced cost at participating MTFs.

  Go to **militaryaudiology.org/rachap-rhapp-locations** for a list of participating MTFs, including some overseas locations. Contact the audiology department of any listed site for more information. Since services cannot be performed remotely, factor in the cost of travel if it should be necessary.

- The VA Health Care Program, which is separate from VA Disability Benefits, may provide hearing aids to qualified vets even with **no service-connected hearing loss.** Chapter 1 has a description of the VA Health Care Program. The author, without any VA-rated disability, obtained <u>free</u> hearing aids through the VA Medical Center in Hawaii in 2022. My story in the next section explains how this was done.

- Lastly, the VA Disability Benefits Program will provide hearing aids at no cost to any veteran with a qualifying service-connected hearing loss. This is within the VA's traditional disability benefits provided to veterans.

The VA also covers battery replacement through both programs, although you could request a model with rechargeable batteries. Learn more about VA hearing aid benefits at: **www.prosthetics.va.gov/psas/hearing_aids.asp**.

Real Life Story: Hearing Aids with VA Health Care

In Chapter 1, we described the VA Health Care Program, in which veterans can obtain care from the VA without any service-connected disability, yet many veterans still remain unaware of this benefit. This is my personal story of obtaining hearing aids at the VA for <u>free</u> without any service-related hearing loss.

I was astonished to learn about this benefit in a Facebook group for veterans. It seemed unbelievable, so I decided to check it out for myself. It takes just a few minutes, and you can apply online at **www.va.gov/health-care/apply/application**. Within weeks, a VA representative called to explain about VA Health Care, explaining that medical benefits are available to veterans <u>without</u> having to apply for a disability rating. The representative was incredibly patient and courteous, spending an hour with me on the phone to answer all my questions.

At the end of the call, he assigned me to a VA primary care physician and scheduled my first appointment. I met with my doctor two weeks later through a video chat from home. Connecting was simple: she sent me a link that launched our online session. We spent 45 minutes discussing my medical history, and she entered all my TRICARE prescriptions into the VA system for future refills by mail. No in-person exam or lab test was needed.

She asked what other specialized care I would like, so I mentioned the need for mental health counseling and help with my hearing loss. She quickly set up appointments for both. The counseling was done via video chat over multiple sessions and was extremely helpful. The hearing test was conducted two months later at the VA medical center in Hawaii. The audiologist concluded that my hearing loss would be alleviated by hearing aids and offered a top-line product by Oticon, a leading brand. On the open market, these would cost over $4,000. The cost to me was <u>zero</u>.

From the time that I joined VA Health Care in August 2021 until I received my hearing aids took seven months. It would have been faster, but COVID and the holidays added some delay, and twice I had to reschedule my appointment.

There were some copayments along the way. Each of my prescription refills was $15. Since TRICARE refills are cheaper, I didn't order any more refills from the VA. The primary care and mental health consultations were free. The audiology exam had a $50 copayment, but the hearing aids were free. If I had met certain financial criteria, such as minimal financial assets or low income, I would not have paid any copayments.

All in all, it was a very good experience for me. My final impression is that everyone in the VA has worked very hard to rebuild a culture of service to our nation's veterans. Instead of long waiting lists and being told "No" as I had expected, I found a very caring and responsive environment where everyone tries to say "Yes." Although I probably won't use VA Health Care much because I am well-covered by TRICARE, it's nice to have that option for things that TRICARE benefits do not cover.

Special Needs/ECHO Program

TRICARE plans include support services to those with special needs. This includes behavioral analysis, skilled nursing (but not Long Term Care), durable medical equipment, and more. Learn about this at **tricare.mil/CoveredServices/SpecialNeeds**.

TRICARE's **Extended Care Health Option (ECHO)** provides supplemental services to **Active Duty Family Members (ADFMs) with qualifying mental or physical disabilities** and offers integrated services and supplies beyond those offered by TRICARE plans. To obtain these benefits, sponsors must sign up for the **Exceptional Family Member Program (EFMP)** through their military branch then register for ECHO with the regional contractor. ECHO coverage is not retroactive, so sign up as soon as possible.

Qualifying ADFMs must be enrolled in TRICARE Prime, Select, or U.S. Family Health Plan. ECHO benefits are available to the following ADFMs with a qualifying condition:

- TRICARE-eligible ADFMs, including family members of National Guard and Reserve members ordered to active duty for more than 30 days.
- Family members who are eligible for continued coverage under the Transitional Assistance Management Program.
- Children or spouses of former service members who were victims of physical or emotional abuse.
- Family members of a deceased active duty sponsor while they are in transitional survivor status.

Conditions to qualify for ECHO coverage include, but are not limited to:

- Autism spectrum disorder
- Moderate or severe intellectual disability
- Serious physical disability
- Extraordinary physical or psychological condition of such complexity that the beneficiary is homebound
- Neuromuscular developmental condition or other condition in an infant or toddler (under age 3) that is expected to precede a diagnosis of moderate or severe intellectual disability or a serious physical disability
- Multiple disabilities, which may qualify if there are two or more disabilities affecting separate body systems

Children may remain eligible for ECHO benefits beyond the usual TRICARE eligibility age limit, provided all the following are true:

- The sponsor remains on active duty.
- The child is incapable of self-support because of a mental or physical incapacity that occurs prior to the loss of eligibility.
- The sponsor provides over 50 percent of the child's financial support.

For more information about EFMP, contact your service branch's EFMP representative. Learn more about ECHO benefits at **www.tricare.mil/Plans/SpecialPrograms/ECHO**. Other resources for those with special needs can be found at **www.militaryonesource.mil/family-relationships**.

Mental Health Coverage

TRICARE offers comprehensive mental health coverage, including inpatient and outpatient care. It is very important to ensure that you visit an "authorized provider" when you seek care. A practitioner holding a certificate, rather than a medical license, is <u>not</u> an authorized TRICARE provider, so their invoices will not be honored. As long as you see a practitioner with a valid medical license from the jurisdiction in which they practice, you should not have a problem.

Following is the list of mental health services that TRICARE covers as of the publication date of this book. For a complete description of mental health coverage and any changes, exclusions, or preconditions that might apply, visit **tricare.mil/CoveredServices/Mental/Treatments**.

<u>Mental Health Covered Services</u>

Applied Behavior Analysis
Autism Spectrum Disorder
Cognitive Rehabilitation Therapy
Drug Testing
Eating Disorder Treatment
Electroconvulsive Therapy
Family Therapy
Gender Dysphoria
Intensive Outpatient Programs
Inpatient Services (Emergency and Non-Emergency)
Management of Withdrawal Symptoms (Detox)
Medication Assisted Treatment
Office Based Opioid Treatment

Opioid Treatment Programs
Partial Hospitalization
Psychoanalysis
Psychological Testing
Psychotherapy
Psychotropic Drugs
Residential Treatment Facility Care
Substance Use Disorder Treatment
Therapeutic Services
Transcranial Magnetic Stimulation

Those in TRICARE Prime usually work with their Primary Care Manager for referrals. Those on non-managed care plans do not need referrals and may see any <u>medically</u> licensed mental health provider they choose to obtain covered services. In a mental health emergency where there is a risk of harm to the patient or those around them, no referral is needed. The patient should obtain emergency care without delay.

While many mental health services are covered, there is also a list of excluded services. This list could change at any time, so contact your regional contractor to confirm coverage at **tricare.mil/CoveredServices/IsItCovered/ MentalHealthExclusions**.

Mental Health Exclusions

Aversion therapy
Behavioral care & supplies related solely to obesity
    and/or weight reduction
Bioenergetic therapy
Biofeedback for psychosomatic conditions
Carbon dioxide therapy
Counseling services (e.g., nutritional, stress
    management, marital therapy, or lifestyle
    modifications)
Custodial nursing care
Diagnostic admissions
Educational programs

Environmental ecological treatments

Experimental procedures

Filial therapy

Guided imagery

Hemodialysis for schizophrenia

Marathon therapy

Megavitamin or orthomolecular therapy

Narcotherapy with LSD

Primal therapy

Psychosurgery

Rolfing

Sedative action electro-stimulation therapy

Sexual dysfunction therapy

Stellate ganglion block for the treatment of Post-Traumatic Stress Disorder

Therapy for developmental disorders (i.e., dyslexia, developmental mathematics/language disorders, developmental articulation disorders)

Training analysis

Transcendental meditation

Z therapy

Residential substance abuse treatment <u>always</u> requires pre-authorization from your regional contractor, whether or not you obtain referral from a PCM. It is always smart to call your regional contractor (e.g., TRICARE East/West, TRICARE Overseas, or TFL) when scheduling care with which you are unfamiliar. Even if you don't require pre-authorization, they can provide helpful tips for finding the most appropriate care and also may be able to direct you to a network provider, which can reduce your out-of-pocket costs.

It is worth restating: **Any provider you visit MUST hold a medical license from the jurisdiction in which he or she practices.** Unlicensed practitioners, such as holistic healers or those holding certificates rather than a medical license, are <u>not</u> covered by TRICARE, and you would pay all costs yourself.

COVID Coverage

TRICARE coverage for COVID testing, treatment, and vaccination continues to evolve. All the information in this section is highly subject to change. Verify current benefits at the links below or by contacting your regional contractor.

Coronavirus continues to mutate and evolve, as outbreaks spring up around the world. Symptoms and transmissibility of the disease also may change, as well as the methods of testing and treatment. Official government websites are your best source of information. To learn more, visit **www.tricare.mil/HealthWellness/ HealthyLiving/Coronavirus**.

COVID Testing

TRICARE covers COVID-19 tests (including at-home tests) when medically necessary and ordered by an authorized provider. Testing solely for work or travel is <u>not</u> a medical necessity and is unlikely to be covered. Read below if you need a COVID test due to military travel orders.

Many communities offer free testing regardless of insurance. Inquire locally to see if testing is available on demand to find alternatives other than TRICARE-covered testing.

Anyone who suspects they have symptoms or exposure to COVID-19 should seek medical care. Your provider will determine the need for a test based on risk, symptoms, and guidance from the Centers for Disease Control and Prevention (CDC). Another resource is the Military Health System (MHS) Nurse Advice Line, where knowledgeable RNs can listen to your concerns and offer the best course of action. Contact information for this free resource is in Chapter 12.

Most medical facilities ask that you **do NOT simply walk in and request a test.** If you have been exposed, you could pass the virus to others at the facility, causing further spread of the virus. Call ahead for instructions <u>before</u> going to any medical facility for COVID testing.

Anyone requiring a test for military travel orders will find instructions for testing in the written orders. You would normally be tested at no cost at an MTF. If you pay for a test at a civilian provider, **retain the receipt and submit a claim on your military travel orders**, <u>not</u> **to TRICARE.** Contact your travel office for further guidance.

There is no copayment for <u>covered</u> COVID-19 tests if you are eligible under TRICARE. If you paid for a covered test and have not been fully reimbursed, submit a supplemental claim for full reimbursement. Call your regional contractor for guidance. Other restrictions and limitations apply for who is covered, and under what circumstances. For a complete list, visit: **tricare.mil/HealthWellness/HealthyLiving/Coronavirus/ Coronavirus-Testing.**

Telemedicine/Telehealth

During the COVID pandemic, TRICARE initiated temporary provisions to include medical consultation remotely by phone or video chat. This extends to all sorts of medical appointments, not just those related to COVID. This can include:

- Primary, routine, and specialty care
- Behavioral care such as family counseling
- Physical or occupational therapy

As always, these consultations must be medically and/or psychologically necessary and appropriate to your condition. You must receive care from an <u>authorized</u> provider. With TRICARE Prime, you will need a referral from your PCM to avoid Point of Service fees. For mental health care, see the preceding section for precautions on selecting a TRICARE-authorized provider; those guidelines apply equally for telemedicine.

TRICARE Around the World

As of this writing, TRICARE is <u>temporarily</u> waiving the copayments, cost-shares, and deductibles for telehealth services received from in-network providers. Enrollees in both TRICARE Prime and Select are eligible, and this waiver of fees is not just for COVID-related matters but for all telehealth services.

In another temporary provision, TRICARE is allowing telemedicine services across state or national borders. Federal, state, or host nation laws must allow out-of-state or international practice. This helps in areas where there is a shortage of local health care services. Your provider's license must allow practice out-of-state. If you are receiving care across international borders, your host nation must permit international practice. ISOS (TRICARE Overseas) may be able to help you research local laws about using telehealth internationally.

COVID Vaccination

The TRICARE vaccination policy continues to evolve. For current information about receiving a vaccination for COVID-19, visit **www.tricare.mil/covidvaccine**.

There are a few salient points that have remained constant:

- CDC or FDA-approved vaccines will be provided to <u>all</u> TRICARE beneficiaries at no cost, in accordance with current CDC guidelines.

- MTFs around the world generally serve the beneficiaries assigned to them for primary care. This includes active duty members, command-sponsored ADFMs who are collocated with their sponsor, and others assigned to that MTF for primary care.

- Those who are not assigned to an MTF for primary care can inquire at any MTF about the availability of vaccine. If they cannot be accommodated, these members have the option to obtain the vaccine from civilian providers off base. Each MTF sets their own policy.

- For retirees living overseas, your best source of information are local or national authorities of your host nation. When, where, and how the vaccine will be offered to foreign nationals like yourself is up to each nation. TRICARE has no influence over this process.

- If obtaining the vaccine from a civilian provider overseas, try to obtain a vaccine approved by the U.S. CDC or FDA. If there are no such vaccines in your area, contact your regional contractor or the MHS Nurse Advice Line for guidance on what will be covered by TRICARE in your area.

- Under the SAVES LIVES Act, signed into law in March 2021, the VA received expanded authority to provide COVID vaccine to U.S. military veterans, their spouses, dependent family members, and caregivers. Locations include the United States, as well as VA facilities and clinics in Puerto Rico, Manila, Guam, American Samoa, and Saipan.

- It is doubtful that U.S. embassies will provide vaccine to Americans abroad, other than the embassy staff.

Dental Coverage

Three dental plans cover TRICARE beneficiaries:

- **Active Duty Dental Plan (ADDP)** is for active duty members as well as activated National Guard and Reservists. This covers the dental needs of military members and is always at no cost. Learn more at **tricare.mil/CoveredServices/Dental/ADDental/ADDP**.

- **TRICARE Dental Plan (TDP)** is for family members of active duty sponsors as well as non-activated Guard or Reserve members and their families. This is optional coverage, provided for a fee. To learn about costs, benefits, and enrollment, visit **www.uccitdp.com/dtwdws/member/landing.xhtml**.

- **The Federal Employees Dental & Vision Insurance Program (FEDVIP)** covers military retirees and their dependents. FEDVIP is not part of TRICARE; it replaces the old TRICARE Retiree Dental Program which ended in 2018. FEDVIP coverage is optional, for a fee. For details, visit **www.benefeds.com**.

- **Survivors of deceased sponsors** may be covered either by TRICARE Dental Survivor Benefit or FEDVIP. For surviving family members:
  - Spouses are eligible for TRICARE Dental Survivor Benefits for three years, beginning on the date of the sponsor's death.
  - Children are eligible until age 21, or age 23 if they are enrolled full time in an accredited college and meet other qualifying conditions.
  - Coverage during this period is 100 percent free to the family members.
  - Learn more at **www.tricare.mil/CoveredServices/ Dental/SurvivorBenefit**.

- **Adult children enrolled in TYA** are not eligible for any dental programs under TRICARE.

For more information, see **tricare.mil/Costs/DentalCosts**.

Expert Tip: Here's a money-saving strategy for veterans with a 100% P&T disability rating from the VA and others who qualify for VA dental care. When enrolling your family for dental coverage through FEDVIP, leave the veteran off the dental plan. The veteran can obtain full dental care at no cost through the VA. By leaving them off the dental plan, you will see a significant drop in the FEDVIP monthly premium. Be sure to confirm first with the local VA that they are able to provide dental services.

Vision Care

Vision benefits depend on which plan you are in, your status (ADSM/ADFM/retiree) and the purchase of optional vision care through FEDVIP. Holding third-party vision insurance does not impact your eye exam eligibility under TRICARE. To learn more about this, visit **tricare.mil/Covered Services/Vision** or go to **www.benefeds.com**.

- **Active Duty Service Members (ADSM)**
  - Full vision care at no cost.
  - Eye exams, glasses, or contacts provided through the MTF, or a network provider with referral.
  - If in Prime Remote, contact your regional contractor for a referral.
  - An ADSM visiting a non-network provider <u>without</u> a referral may be responsible for the entire cost. **NOTE:** This is one of the rare instances where free care for ADSM is <u>not</u> guaranteed. This is avoidable simply by getting a referral beforehand.

- **ADFM** (including family members of activated Guard or Reservists):
  - One routine eye exam per year regardless of TRICARE plan.
  - Glasses and contacts are not provided via any ADFM TRICARE plan.
  - More complete vision coverage, including glasses, contacts, and discounted laser eye surgery, is available through the optional FEDVIP Program.

- **All other beneficiaries:**
  - One eye exam every two years in TRICARE Prime.
  - In USFHP, contact the provider for details.
  - In all other plans, routine eye exams are not covered.

TRICARE Around the World

- o Glasses and contacts are not included in any of these plans.

Children from age three until the sixth birthday (ages 3-5) can receive biannual eye exams under their well-child benefits. There is no cost, regardless of plan.

All TRICARE plans include ophthalmic services for the diagnosis and treatment of eye disorders. Ophthalmology covers, for example, the diagnosis and treatment of cataracts. Contact your regional contractor for more information about such services.

Travel Expenses

<u>Non-active duty</u> beneficiaries in Prime or Prime Remote may be eligible for travel and lodging reimbursement under certain circumstances. To qualify, <u>all</u> the following must be true:

- Cannot be on active duty
- Must have a referral from the PCM
- Must be on Prime or Prime Remote
- The specialist must be more than 100 miles from the PCM's office.

If all four apply, you may qualify for the Prime Travel Benefit. Learn more at **tricare.mil/primetravel** or ask your regional contractor for more information.

Air Ambulance/Medical Evacuation

TRICARE offers *limited* coverage for medical evacuation or air ambulance. If you want more comprehensive or flexible coverage, you should research private commercial policies. For TRICARE air evacuation coverage:

- Transport must be **medically necessary.**

- Air transport will take you to the **NEAREST hospital** that can safely provide the care you need. Most likely, this will <u>not</u> be a U.S. military facility.

- **They will not transport you to the U.S.** unless that is the nearest place for the type of care you need.

- For ADSM/ADFM enrollees in Prime or Prime Remote, International SOS can coordinate transportation and provide a cashless transaction. All others must pay for the transport upfront, which can be extremely costly, and then submit a claim for reimbursement.

- If it is determined that the transport was not medically necessary, **your claim may be denied.**

As you can see, TRICARE coverage has severe limitations. If air evacuation coverage is important to you, consider purchasing a commercial policy. Coverage can be purchased on a yearly basis or for short vacations, with or without its own medical coverage. It is far cheaper to purchase without medical coverage and rely on TRICARE for the medical portion of your needs.

Many commercial packages:
- Guarantee your return to the U.S. to continue your medical care.

- Do not require a finding of medical necessity.

- Require little or no upfront funds from you, other than your prepaid premium.

Join our Facebook group *"TRICARE Around the World"* to discuss this further and to get recommendations from other members. You can learn more about medical transport at **tricare.mil/CoveredServices/IsItCovered/AirEvacuation**.

Expert Tip: The terms "air ambulance" or "air evacuation" also may be called "medical evacuation" or "repatriation." The term "repatriation" can refer either to the medical transport of a patient or the return of remains after death. Some policies will include medical coverage while others are for transport only. Clarify these terms with the insurer when comparing policies.

TRICARE on Cruise Ships

You might be surprised to learn that TRICARE can be used on cruise ships. It works just the same as any other setting: Get the medical care you need and pay the cruise line. **Be sure to get an itemized receipt and medical report for your claim.** If you will be hospitalized, notify your regional contractor at the first opportunity. Even at sea, you should be able call or send a message. Use an app like Skype or Vonage to avoid the high cost of voice calls at sea or internationally.

If you have travel medical insurance, then TRICARE is the second payer. File your claim first with the travel policy. Once you receive the Explanation of Benefits (EOB), submit a claim to TRICARE for unpaid costs and attach the EOB to your claim.

Three major precautions apply:

- TRICARE has a reimbursement limit for all types of care. Medical fees at sea are extraordinarily high, so it is quite possible to exceed TRICARE cost limits onboard a ship.
- The ship's location can impact your costs. If the ship is in a U.S. port or U.S. territorial waters, you fall within TRICARE East or West, and Medicare will work. Outside U.S. territorial waters, you cannot use Medicare. If you are near the U.S. coast, ask the cruise operator for the precise location.
- For those in a TRICARE Prime plan, obtaining routine care without a referral is Point of Service care, with

higher deductibles and copayments. For details about POS, see Chapter 6 under TRICARE Prime.

Expert Tip: If you become sick on a cruise, consider obtaining care ashore rather than onboard. Medical fees aboard ship may exceed TRICARE reimbursement limits while care ashore is likely to be far cheaper. You will have to judge whether a delay in treatment is advisable and if the quality of care at the port-of-call meets your standards. If possible, contact the MHS Nurse Advice Line for advice. See Chapter 12 for more information about the Nurse Advice Line.

Real Life Story: Sleep Study & CPAP

Twice as a military retiree on TRICARE, I have conducted a sleep study and obtained a CPAP (Continuous Positive Airway Pressure) machine. The first instance, in 2015, was as a retiree in TRICARE Prime at Tripler Army Medical Center in Hawaii. The second, in 2020, was at a private hospital in Bangkok, Thailand, using TRICARE Overseas Select.

CPAP therapy alleviates symptoms of Obstructive Sleep Apnea (OSA), a disorder in which breathing is interrupted during sleep. OSA can be diagnosed and quantified with a sleep study. There are two ways this is done:

- In a specially-equipped hospital room where the patient's breathing, heartbeat, blood oxygen level, snoring, and body movements are monitored through the night. This is the type of study that I had done in Thailand.

- A far less extensive study with a take-home device provided by your doctor. This is what I did in Hawaii where the hospital study is offered only to active duty.

If offered an at-home sleep study, ask for a referral to a civilian provider for the more thorough in-hospital method. In 2015, I was not knowledgeable enough to make that request.

TRICARE Around the World

In Thailand, using a specially-equipped sleep study hospital room, I slept the first half of the night without the CPAP in order to create a baseline of my condition. Then I was awakened and fitted with the mask to assess how well my symptoms were alleviated by the CPAP. The overnight stay is not considered to be inpatient care, because you are not admitted for treatment, so your TRICARE copayment will not be based on the rates for inpatient care. With the at-home monitoring device, a before-and-after comparison is not performed.

Based on the results of each study, I was issued a prescription for a CPAP. In my experience, the sale of CPAP machines and masks is tightly regulated. I could not obtain the machine or supplies without a prescription. Perhaps the practice is different in other countries.

With TRICARE Prime in Hawaii, I was not given a choice of which CPAP device I got. Tripler sent me to a local supplier who had a CPAP ready for me. It was preset to the parameters my doctor had prescribed, and the vendor provided a few hurried minutes of instruction. For five years, I hoped that the settings were good because I didn't know how to verify or change them.

In contrast, when I got my second CPAP in Thailand using TRICARE Select, TRICARE Overseas told me to choose a machine from any vendor and then submit a claim. I selected a New Zealand brand from a supplier in Bangkok. TRICARE Select covers 75% of the cost of Durable Medical Equipment (DME) from non-network providers, and that is exactly what was refunded to me. At the time, it was the largest claim I had yet submitted with TRICARE Overseas, and it was a great relief to see that the process worked as advertised.

Unlike my experience in Hawaii, the vendor representative in Thailand came to my home, set up the machine, and provided hands-on instruction. She let me borrow a CPAP for two nights to make sure it was satisfactory to me. Once I made the purchase decision, she came back to finalize all the paperwork and set up a datalink to my iPhone. Customer support was vastly superior to my previous experience in the States.

Many CPAP machines can transmit data so that your doctor or insurance provider can monitor its effectiveness. Machines from the States often use a cellular connection that works only in North America. Since my family lives a nomadic lifestyle, I wanted a CPAP that could send data directly to my smartphone by Wi-Fi or Bluetooth, without reliance on a cellular network. This narrowed my choices considerably, but I did eventually find one that connects with my phone by Bluetooth. Each morning I can view the results of my sleep therapy on the app. The data can also be shared with my doctor and the vendor representative, who provides ongoing support. Join our Facebook group if you want to know specifics of my purchase.

With TRICARE Prime, I did not own the machine; I had a small copayment each month to lease. I also made copayments to buy masks and hoses, which were mailed automatically to my home. With TRICARE Select, I own the machine because I bought it outright. There are no monthly fees, although I do pay a 25 percent cost-share for hoses and masks. Because of the ability to choose the machine I wanted, plus the excellent customer support that was given, I found my experience with TRICARE Select in Thailand to be far superior to what I went through with TRICARE Prime in the States.

5
Finding A Provider

ONE OF THE THINGS THAT MEMBERS FIND MOST CONFUSING about TRICARE is locating health care providers whether in the States, or living as an expat overseas, or while traveling. Recurring questions we hear are: *Who can I see, when can I see them, and how do I find them?* The answers are far easier than you might think, as you will see.

This chapter describes the different types of providers and other assistance available to you worldwide. You can read TRICARE's complete guide to finding and choosing doctors at **www.tricare.mil/FindDoctor/Traveling**.

Authorized Providers

The TRICARE website says that you must see "TRICARE-authorized providers," but how do you figure out who these providers are? Is there a list somewhere? A search engine?

- **Within the U.S.**, one way to locate providers is to click "Find a Doctor" on the TRICARE homepage. This search tool can find providers by U.S. ZIP Code in any number of medical specialties. Our experience is that the search engine doesn't always work well, so we have come to rely on other strategies as explained in the next section.

- **Outside the U.S.**, the term "authorized" is not used. In TRICARE's words, you may visit **any provider who is "licensed by a state, accredited by a national organization, or meets other standards of the medical community."** In other words, if your overseas provider holds a medical license where they practice, they are an "authorized provider." *There is no list.*

This is game-changing! Once you understand that you can visit virtually <u>any</u> international hospital, clinic, or doctor that is medically licensed, using TRICARE around the world suddenly becomes so much easier.

Naturally, there are exclusions and exceptions. For instance, members of Prime plans need referrals or pre-authorization for routine care to avoid high Point of Service fees. The Philippines has its own unique search engine for finding providers (see Chapter 8). You might find it advantageous to seek out network providers – which can be found in many cities around the world – to reduce your costs. But other than that, TRICARE is largely demystified once you understand how broadly accessible it is wherever you go.

Finding a PCM or Family Practice Doctor

If you are in a TRICARE Prime plan, you will be assigned a Primary Care Manager (PCM) during your enrollment process. Your PCM is the doctor or other health care professional who you will initially see for most non-emergency health needs. They will provide referrals to specialists when needed. Your PCM may be at an MTF or a civilian facility, but all your care will be handled within the TRICARE network, making health management quite simple. For this reason, TRICARE Prime is called a "managed care plan."

Non-Prime plans are not managed care, and you will <u>not</u> have a PCM. This is also referred to as self-directed care because you are empowered to make many healthcare decisions on your own. Some people say "PCM" when referring to doctors in non-Prime plans, but this is incorrect. What they are really referring to is a family practice doctor, but this is not the same as a PCM under managed care plans. With self-directed care, you can bypass your family doctor if, for example, you want to see an audiologist or a dermatologist for covered care.

Despite this, there are times when it is prudent to see your family doctor first, before going to a specialist. This could be in cases where you'll be getting lab tests that should be interpreted by your doctor, such as blood tests, cancer screening, X-rays, or other medical imaging. Labs that perform these tests normally do it only when ordered by a physician; they do not take walk-in patients. This is a safeguard to help avoid unnecessary or inappropriate tests and so that test results will be properly interpreted and explained to you upon completion.

Within the United States, how do you find a family doctor or general practitioner with TRICARE Select and other self-directed plans? You can use the TRICARE Provider Finder tool but, as mentioned earlier, this does not always work well. Here in Hawaii, which is crawling with network providers, it finds none within 20 miles of my home – almost the entire island of Oahu. I know without question that this is incorrect.

What you can do instead is work the problem in reverse. First, choose a nearby hospital that you like: one with strong customer reviews, offering comprehensive services including a 24-hour emergency room, and is a network provider for your TRICARE plan. You might have to call them to confirm that they are in-network.

Once you have found a suitable hospital, review their list of affiliated doctors. Most hospitals have an online directory. These are doctors in private practice, not necessarily located at the hospital but who have admitting privileges with access to the hospital's network of specialists. In our town, we found a great number of family practice doctors just minutes from our home that are aligned with the local hospital.

Next, sort by specialty, such as general medicine, family practice, pediatrics, etc. Some clinics may not be accepting new patients, further narrowing your choices. Once you find a doctor you like, call them to register as a new patient and double-check that they are a network provider for your specific plan. This

83

"holds your place" with that practice and aligns you with the hospital's network of labs and specialists, most of whom will be TRICARE network providers. When you follow these steps, you may never see a claim form again!

Overseas, it will be somewhat different. You are not going to find a vast network of TRICARE providers to meet all of your needs. In fact, you will be lucky to find any in-network provider at all. If you are fortunate enough to find a full-service hospital or medical center that is a TRICARE network provider, latch onto them! They will take good care of you, charging you only your cost-share, and send the remainder of the bill to TRICARE. It simplifies your life, and you will never have to submit a claim.

The more likely course overseas is that there will be no network provider near you. In this case, find a hospital or clinic that you like, preferably one who accepts credit cards. (Yes, there are cash-only medical providers in many parts of the world.) You see your practitioner for care, pay the bill in full, and then submit a claim for reimbursement. Chapters 10 and 11 cover this process in detail.

Network Providers

When possible, you should use TRICARE network providers. Within the United States, this is especially advantageous for several reasons:

- TRICARE network providers stateside are rather plentiful, so there is a good chance that one is nearby.

- With health care so expensive in the United States, paying an in-network flat fee will be much cheaper than paying a percentage of the bill for non-network care.

- After you pay the deductible and copayment, the provider will send the remaining bill to the regional contractor for payment. This means you pay less money upfront and will not have to submit a claim.

To find a network provider, go to **tricare.mil** and click on "Find a Doctor." You may also inquire at the nearest MTF, ask within the local military community, talk to your regional contractor or the Nurse Advice Line, or call any provider and ask if they are in-network. **Note**: Be sure to specify which plan you are in because some providers might be in-network for Prime, but <u>not</u> for Select (or vice versa).

Outside the U.S., finding a network provider can be more challenging. There may not be any in your area, or they might be in-network for some situations (e.g., inpatient care or active duty only) but not for others. The TRICARE Overseas call centers are often unable to tell you who is in-network, and even the hospital staff might not be sure. If you instead visit a non-network provider, you will pay the bill in full at discharge and be reimbursed when you file your claim.

From discussions in our Facebook group, we are aware of network providers in Thailand, Germany, France, UK, South Korea, Italy, and Japan. There are bound to be some in other countries as well, if you can find them. The greatest source of information is the military expat community.

In the Philippines, "Preferred" providers are roughly equivalent to network providers. They are found in the major urban areas of Metro Manila, Subic, and Clark/Angeles City. See Chapter 8 for more information about finding providers in the Philippines.

If you are in one of the TRICARE Prime options, your PCM may refer you to network specialists as needed. If your PCM refers you to a non-network provider, you will be charged only the network copay because you have a referral. If you are in Prime and see a specialist <u>without</u> a referral – even a network provider – this is called Point of Service (POS) and it will be very expensive for you. Learn more about POS in Chapter 6.

In TRICARE Select, you can visit network or non-network providers at your discretion. With a network provider, your copayment will be a flat fee. With non-network, your cost-share is a percentage of the bill. This means that for less expensive visits, a network provider could cost <u>more</u> than a non-network provider. See my Real Life Story about this below.

<u>Real Life Story</u>: How can a network provider end up costing more than a non-network one? We once went to an emergency room in Bangkok. The bill was $120, and we expected our share to be 25% of that; just $30 (since our family deductible for the year had already been met). Once the claim settled, however, our share was $50. When I asked why, ISOS said it was because we had gone to a network hospital, and the network copayment was a flat $50. If we had gone to a non-network provider, we would have had a 25 percent cost-share, or $30.

Fortunately for us, this was an inexpensive rookie mistake costing us just $20. This "inverted" price structure happens only with smaller bills, below $150 or so. Overseas, where care is so cheap, it is quite possible for a non-network provider to cost less than a network one.

Non-Network Providers

Non-network providers:

- Have no formal agreement with your regional contractor or with TRICARE.
- Are unlikely to file claims for you.
- Will require full payment from you, after which you will submit a claim for reimbursement.

Within the category of non-network providers, there are **Participating** and **Non-Participating providers**. Participating providers agree to accept the TRICARE allowable charge as full payment, so you won't be stuck with excess fees <u>not</u> covered by TRICARE. Non-participating providers have no such agreement, so it is possible that their fees can exceed TRICARE's allowable reimbursement limits. You would <u>not</u> be reimbursed for the excess fees.

Outside the U.S., the vast majority of providers are non-network. You pay the bill at discharge and submit a claim at your earliest convenience. Once you practice this skill a few times, you can reasonably expect to get your reimbursement in just a few weeks. See Chapters 10 and 11 for details of filing claims.

Emergency Care

If you are reading this because you are in the midst of a medical emergency and trying to figure out what to do – ***STOP!*** Put the book down, call an ambulance, or go to the nearest emergency room. Emergency care is covered under all TRICARE plans worldwide without exception. If you are unsure if your situation qualifies as an emergency, contact the MHS Nurse Advice Line; they will advise what to do and how your TRICARE benefits will work. Visit **mhsnurseadviceline.com**.

If your concern is about how to pay a potentially large bill for emergency care, call your TRICARE regional contractor once the crisis has been dealt with; they may be able to coordinate directly with the hospital for payment. Phone numbers for TRICARE regional call centers are listed under "Global Resources" in Chapter 12. The good news is, if you are overseas the cost of emergency care is likely to be far less than you are used to in the United States… sometimes just a few hundred dollars.

Emergency care is covered by TRICARE… period! No one will second-guess your choice of hospital. Bring this book with you and continue reading when you have time, but for now the priority is to get the care you need, whether for yourself or a loved one.

Urgent Care Clinics

Urgent Care is medical care needed for a non-emergency illness or injury that:

- Is not a threat to life, limb, or eyesight.
- Needs attention before it becomes a serious risk to health.
- Should receive attention within 24 hours to avoid further risk or complications.

Examples may include conditions like a sprained ankle, infection, minor cuts or burns, or fever. **If you are unsure whether urgent care is warranted, call the MHS Nurse Advice Line to talk with a registered nurse.**

The rules governing access to urgent care depend largely on the status of the patient:

- An ADSM who lives in a Prime Service Area should visit an MTF for urgent care or call the MHS Nurse Advice Line for assistance.
- An ADSM in Prime Remote can visit any TRICARE-authorized clinic without referral.
- Retirees, their family members and ADFMs do not need a referral.
- Beneficiaries in USFHP should consult their provider's website for guidance.
- Remember: TRICARE Plus and Direct Care Only (DCO) will **not** reimburse care from civilian providers, which includes Urgent Care Clinics.

For further details, visit **tricare.mil/CoveredServices/IsItCovered/UrgentCare**.

Real Life Story: When we moved to our home in Hawaii, we discovered two urgent care clinics in the neighborhood. Dropping in, we found that both were TRICARE network providers, and one was affiliated with the same hospital as our family doctor. This clinic is where we go for our more immediate needs, rather than waiting weeks to see our doctor. The clinic charges a $32 copay for each visit, and we never have to file a claim. Because they are affiliated with the same hospital network as our family doctor, our medical records are integrated between our providers. It is a great system; the concept of urgent care in America has evolved in many positive ways in recent years.

Nurse Advice Line

One of the most useful resources is the Military Health System (MHS) Nurse Advice Line. This free service gives you 24/7 access to very knowledgeable nurses who work at MHS, the parent organization of TRICARE. They are trained in assessing symptoms and health-related issues, and you can speak to a pediatric nurse if calling about a child. They understand your TRICARE benefits in depth and can direct you to the most appropriate health resources in your community. If you are unsure whether your health issue is covered by TRICARE or who to see for medical care, the Nurse Advice Line can help.

Visit **mhsnurseadviceline.com** or call 1-800-TRICARE (874-2273). There are some tricks to accessing the help line from overseas which are explained in Chapter 12 in the section titled "MHS Nurse Advice Line."

Direct Billing Providers

A common misperception is to confuse network providers with those who direct bill. This misunderstanding might be costing you money. Direct-billing providers – even if they are non-network – will charge you your deductible and copayment, then bill TRICARE for the rest. To calculate this amount, they must contact your regional contractor to determine whether you have satisfied your deductible for the year and find out your cost-share. If you have reached your catastrophic cap for the year, you may not have to pay anything at all.

TRICARE Around the World

It is difficult to know which providers will direct bill since TRICARE does not keep a list, and providers can change their mind about it. Direct-bill providers do not need permission from TRICARE to bill directly; it is simply a business decision on their part, and you may be able to persuade them try. Your best source of information about this is our Facebook group and from the military expats in your area.

Real Life Story: I was fortunate enough to find a direct-billing hospital for eye surgery in Pattaya, Thailand in 2020. The procedure cost around $10,000, but my family had nearly reached our catastrophic cap for the year. The international insurance office of the Thai hospital called the TRICARE Overseas regional office in Singapore; confirmed that the procedure was covered; calculated my copayment up to the cap, and I ended up paying just a few hundred dollars. The rest of the bill was sent to TRICARE, and I did not have to deal with billing or claims.

Expert Tip: Don't hesitate to ask your hospital to bill TRICARE directly, especially if you are facing expensive inpatient care. It is best to coordinate this in advance of your treatment, but if that is not possible, the hospital's insurance/billing office can send a representative to your room to discuss it. Larger hospitals are skilled in dealing with insurance carriers from all over the world. If they agree to bill TRICARE directly, they will call your regional contractor to confirm your coverage. You will pay only your deductible and cost-share and the remaining bill will be sent to TRICARE. If you have reached your catastrophic cap, you may have no out-of-pocket costs at all!

Point of Service Option

Point of Service (POS) is an option for enrollees in any Prime plan (Prime, Prime Remote, or TYA-Prime) to receive routine (non-emergency) care without a referral.

With the POS option, members can expect:

- A higher deductible than normal.

- A 50 percent copay after meeting the POS deductible.

- More stringent limits on allowable costs, which may increase the member's copay if the limit is exceeded.

The most important financial impact is that **POS fees do not count towards your annual catastrophic cap.** This means that there is **NO LIMIT** on how much you might have to pay. Use POS judiciously or – better yet – not at all.

POS fees do not apply to:

- ADSM, for whom care is always free.

- Anyone on a non-Prime plan.

- A Prime member who obtains care with a referral from their PCM.

- Emergency care and, in most cases, urgent care.

The POS option is discussed further in Chapter 6 in the section about TRICARE Prime.

Overseas Residents Visiting the USA

If you live overseas and are planning to visit the U.S., there are some things that you should know beforehand. Members of Prime or Prime Remote should obtain any routine care <u>before</u> travels begin, including prescription refills. For routine care while traveling, Prime members should seek pre-approval from TRICARE Overseas or a referral from your PCM. Approval is not always granted.

Those on Overseas Select may visit any authorized provider in the U.S. for routine, urgent or emergency care, just as they would in their overseas location. Remember that in the States, network providers are far more plentiful than overseas, meaning your out-of-pocket costs can be less.

TRICARE Around the World

Members in TRICARE for Life (TFL) have an added advantage when visiting the States because Medicare starts working as soon as you enter the country. No referral is needed. As long as you visit a Medicare provider, your Medicare cost-shares are covered by TFL, and you end up paying nothing. This is why many overseas members in TFL periodically return to the States to catch up on expensive medical care. This also gives you a chance to renew prescriptions from a U.S. doctor, which Express Scripts can then refill by mail if you have access to an APO or FPO address abroad (except in Germany, which does not allow medications by mail).

Stateside Residents Traveling Abroad

Let's look at the opposite situation: What if you are enrolled in a stateside plan and need care while traveling overseas? If this happens to you, call an ambulance, go to an emergency room or visit any licensed health care provider without delay. **For those in a Prime plan, notify TRICARE Overseas by phone within 24 hours of obtaining emergency care or being admitted as an inpatient.** ISOS might be able to arrange bill payment for Prime members, reducing your need for cash. This notification is not needed if you are in TRICARE Select or TFL. Contact info can be found in Chapter 12.

If you are unsure as to what warrants urgent or emergency care, call the MHS Nurse Advice Line. A friendly, informed nurse will answer all your TRICARE questions and can advise where to go for care. This line is open 24/7/365. See Chapter 12 for tips on using the Nurse Advice Line.

Active duty members should seek treatment at an MTF when traveling overseas, if possible, but don't let this delay emergency care. In emergencies, seek the nearest care. For urgent care, you should not have to drive more than 30 minutes. There will be no cost to ADSMs, even if you must initially pay out of pocket. After submitting a claim, you will be fully reimbursed.

6
TRICARE Plans

THIS CHAPTER PROVIDES A SUMMARY of each TRICARE plan. Visit **tricare.mil/Plans/HealthPlans** for complete and current information.

Each TRICARE plan is either **managed or non-managed care**. They are also designated as either **premium-based or fee-based**. Knowing the designation of your plan will help you to better understand its cost structure and how to use your benefits.

- **Managed care plans** are TRICARE Prime, Prime Remote, TRICARE Young Adult (Prime), and U.S. Family Health Plan (USFHP). With managed care, you are assigned a Primary Care Manager (PCM) who is usually your first stop, other than emergencies. When needed, your PCM will refer you to a specialist. If you get specialty care without a referral from your PCM, you will incur significantly higher costs.

- **Non-managed care plans**, also called **self-directed care**, consists of all plans not listed above. Under non-managed care, you do not have a PCM. You can choose your own providers and make appointments without referral. Fees and payment terms vary depending on your plan and whether you see a network or a non-network provider. It is common for beneficiaries to choose a family doctor whom they will see regularly, but this is not a requirement under self-directed care.

- **Fee-based plans** are government-subsidized and are generally quite affordable. Members pay an enrollment fee each month, or no fee at all (for active duty families). The amount of the fee is set by legislation. Prime and Select are examples of fee-based plans. Monthly fees and deductibles count towards the family's catastrophic cap.

- **Premium-based plans** are not government-subsidized. The full cost of insurance is borne by enrollees in these plans. Cost may rival that of commercial plans on the open market, but still may be the most affordable option. If premium-based is your only option, it would be wise to shop in the ACA marketplace to make sure TRICARE is your best alternative. Compare not just the premium but also the deductible, copayment, and catastrophic cap. Examples of premium-based plans are TRICARE Young Adult and TRICARE Retired Reserve. Monthly premiums do not count towards a family's annual catastrophic cap.

In choosing a TRICARE plan, members often focus on cost, but **just as important is whether you would feel more comfortable in a managed or non-managed care setting.** Would you prefer seeing a PCM who can make referrals for you, or would you find it easier to make your own health care arrangements? Those transitioning from military service often default to TRICARE Prime because it's what they are used to from their military days. Join our Facebook group to chat with others about what it's like to be in a self-directed plan like TRICARE Select.

The remainder of this chapter describes each of the TRICARE plans to give you a better sense of eligibility and how the plans operate. Costs are explained in Chapter 7.

TRICARE Prime

Overview

TRICARE Prime is a **fee-based, managed-care plan**. You will be assigned to a Primary Care Manager (PCM) who you will see first for any health needs (other than for urgent or emergency care). The PCM will either treat you or make a referral to see a specialist. Getting the referral set up normally takes a few days. Your care will be either at an MTF or a network provider, which means you will never have to submit a claim. Retiree families might have a small copayment for each visit; active duty families will not.

TRICARE Prime offers what is known as a Point of Service (POS) option. This allows beneficiaries to receive care from a TRICARE-authorized provider other than their PCM <u>without</u> a referral. However, this can be **quite costly** and should generally be avoided. **See the section below on the POS Option.**

Who is Eligible for Prime?
- Active duty service members and their families
- Retired service members and their families (stateside only)
- Activated Guard/Reserve members and their families
- Non-activated Guard/Reserve members and their families who qualify for care under the Transitional Assistance Management Program (TAMP)
- Retired Guard/Reserve members after age 60 and their families
- Survivors of deceased sponsors
- Medal of Honor recipients and their families
- Qualified former spouses

TRICARE Around the World

Limitations

- Must live within a Prime Service Area (near an MTF) or sign a waiver for distance restrictions.
- Available overseas only to ADSM, ADFM, activated Guard/Reserve members and their families. All others can participate stateside only.
- Those over 65 must join TRICARE for Life (TFL).
- Adult children until age 21, or to 23 with qualifying college enrollment. See below for more on TYA.

Point of Service (POS) Option

The POS option allows beneficiaries of TRICARE Prime who are <u>not</u> active duty to see a TRICARE-authorized provider other than their PCM without a referral. This can be quite expensive, however, so use it judiciously. For a full explanation, go to: **tricare.mil/Costs/POS**.

- There is a special POS deductible of $300 (individual) or $600 (family). You must pay this amount before your TRICARE cost-sharing begins.
- Cost-share is 50 percent of TRICARE allowable charges, and possibly more for non-network providers.
- **<u>Warning!</u> POS expenses do <u>not</u> count towards your family's catastrophic cap, so there is <u>NO</u> <u>upper limit on your out-of-pocket costs</u>.**

<u>Real Life Story:</u> In our Facebook group, one young mother shared how she inadvertently scheduled childbirth at a network provider without the proper referral from her PCM. This put her into the Point of Service option, and TRICARE assessed her half the cost of childbirth, about $13,000. Had she gotten the correct referral, her cost would have been $0. As of this writing, she is still fighting the decision. It's been an uphill battle and would not have been a problem with the proper referrals.

TRICARE Prime Remote
(Stateside)

Overview

TRICARE Prime Remote is a **fee-based, managed-care plan**. It is intended for active duty members and their families when assigned to a remote location, far from any MTF. Members in Prime Remote will choose a PCM from within the civilian community. The PCM should be a network provider, if available, otherwise you will choose a non-network physician. The PCM is your first stop for any non-emergency care. They can refer you for specialty care, if needed.

Like Prime, Prime Remote offers the Point of Service (POS) option. This allows ADFMs to receive care from a TRICARE-authorized provider other than their PCM without a referral, but costs will be much higher. See the section above for details on the POS option.

Who is Eligible?

- ADSM <u>must</u> enroll in Prime Remote if TRICARE Prime is not available where they live.

- ADFM, if they are command-sponsored and collocated with their sponsor.

- Activated National Guard and Reserve members ordered to active duty service for more than 31 days in a row.

- Activated Guard/Reserve family members if they live in a designated remote location when the sponsor is activated and continue to reside at that address.

Limitations

- Participant must live outside a Prime Service Area (PSA).
- Prime Remote is not available to retirees.

TRICARE Prime Remote (Overseas)

Overview

TRICARE Prime Remote Overseas is a **fee-based, managed-care plan** for active duty and <u>command-sponsored family members</u> in designated remote overseas locations. Because you will not be near an MTF, members will choose a PCM in the civilian community. Your PCM should be a network provider, if one is available, otherwise you will choose a non-network physician. The PCM is your first stop for any non-emergency care. They can refer you for specialty care, if needed.

Like Prime, Prime Remote Overseas offers the Point of Service (POS) option. This allows beneficiaries to receive care from a TRICARE-authorized provider other than their PCM without a referral, but costs will be much higher. See the section above for details on the POS option.

Who is Eligible?
- Active duty service members
- Activated National Guard/Reserve members
- Command-sponsored family members of eligible sponsors

Limitations
- Must live outside a Prime Service Area (PSA)
- Not available to retirees

TRICARE Select

Overview

TRICARE Select is a **fee-based, non-managed care plan** available worldwide to qualified members. You can see any authorized provider of your choosing without referral. ADFMs worldwide can enroll in Select if they so choose. We have had reports in our social media groups of ADFMs being pressured to sign up for Prime even though they prefer Select. If you are an active duty family member, you can enroll in Select, even if you are told otherwise. TRICARE Select offers greater freedom of choice about your healthcare providers, which is why some beneficiaries prefer it. If this is important to you, **stand your ground** if anyone is saying you "must" be in Prime.

For retirees under age 65 living overseas or living in the States outside of a Prime Service Area, TRICARE Select will be their only enrollment option.

With Select, you will not be assigned a PCM, although you can choose to have a family doctor. You may see network or non-network providers. Network providers will charge only your deductible and cost-share and then bill TRICARE for the rest; you will not have to submit a claim. With a non-network provider, it is likely that you will have to pay the entire bill upfront and submit a claim for partial reimbursement. See Chapter 5 for our discussion of network providers, both overseas and in the U.S.

Navigator is a specialized resource only for members in TRICARE Select, designed to assist those with complex medical needs. Administered by Accolade, Navigator is available to those who meet the following criteria:

- Living in the United States
- Two or more complex medical conditions such as asthma, cancer, depression, diabetes, or heart disease
- Claims totaling $100,000 a year or more

Under Navigator, you are assigned a nurse who will help you understand and coordinate your care. There is no additional charge for this service. **Navigator is a pilot program, so it may not be offered indefinitely.** To learn more, search for "Navigator" in the search box on the TRICARE main page or call Accolade at 1-833-400-9603.

Who is Eligible for TRICARE Select?

- Active duty family members (ADFM)
- Retired service members and their families, under 65
- Family members of activated Guard/Reserve members
- Non-activated Guard/Reserve members and their families who qualify for the Transitional Assistance Management Program (TAMP)
- Retired Guard/Reserve members over age 60 and their families
- Survivors of deceased sponsors
- Medal of Honor recipients and their families
- Qualified former spouses

Limitations

- Active duty members, including activated Guard and Reserve, cannot enroll in Select.
- Participants over age 65 must join TRICARE for Life (TFL). Some exceptions apply. Read about TFL below.

U.S. Family Health Plan

Overview

USFHP is a **fee-based, managed care plan**, a form of TRICARE Prime. It is offered through community-based, non-profit health providers around the Washington D.C./Maryland area, New York/New England, Southeast Texas/Southwest Louisiana, and the Pacific Northwest. Enrollees will be assigned a PCM who normally will be the first stop for care.

Some USFHP providers offer benefits beyond the normal TRICARE Prime offerings. This might include vision care, dental services, or gym membership at no extra charge. Other than that, **pricing of USFHP is identical to Prime.** To learn more, visit **www.tricare.mil/usfhp** or **www.usfhp.net**.

Who is Eligible for USFHP?

- Active duty family members
- Retired service members and their families under age 65
- Family members of activated Guard/Reserve members
- Non-activated Guard/Reserve members and their families who qualify for Transitional Assistance Management Program (TAMP)
- Retired Guard/Reserve members at age 60 and their families
- Survivors of deceased sponsors
- Medal of Honor recipients and their families
- Qualified former spouses

Limitations

- Active duty members may not participate
- Until October 1, 2012, USFHP was available to Medicare-eligible beneficiaries, age 65 years and older. USFHP is no longer accepting Medicare-eligible members, but existing enrollees can remain in the plan.
- New Medicare-eligible beneficiaries, age 65 and older, must enroll in TRICARE for Life.

TRICARE for Life/Medicare

Overview

TRICARE for Life (TFL), a **fee-based, non-managed care plan**, is a Medicare wrap-around for beneficiaries who are enrolled in Medicare Parts A and B. Although TRICARE asserts that enrollment in TFL is automatic when you join Medicare, this doesn't always work perfectly. We strongly advise you to follow up with TRICARE to ensure that your enrollment for TFL has been accurately completed once you join Medicare and that fees for your previous plan are no longer auto-paid.

- **Within the United States and U.S. territories**, contact Wisconsin Physician Services (WPS). Their website is: **www.tricare4u.com**.

- **Overseas**, contact International SOS (ISOS). Their website is: **www.tricare-overseas.com**.

See the notes at the end of this section for certain exceptions to TFL enrollment for ADSM or ADFM over age 65, working seniors, and others.

Having a family member turn 65 is a Qualifying Life Event (QLE). This means that <u>every</u> member of the family can change plans, if they so choose, when <u>any</u> family member turns 65. See Chapter 3 for information about QLEs.

Specifics on using TFL depend on status and where you are located:

- **In the U.S. and U.S. territories**, Medicare is first payer; TFL will pay any remaining costs. This is generally a claim-free procedure with zero out-of-pocket costs for authorized care.

- **Outside the U.S.**, Medicare can't be used, so TRICARE is first payer. In this case, TFL operates very much like TRICARE Select. You can see any medically-licensed provider without referral. Members normally will pay the bill upfront and submit a claim to TRICARE Overseas unless they find a network provider or one who will direct-bill to TRICARE. There is a misperception among retirees that TFL members living internationally are in TRICARE Select. That is not true: they remain in TFL and there are some pricing differences between TFL and Select. The two plans are very similar, but they are not identical.

- **If you enroll in Medicare Advantage**, coordination with TFL is not as automatic. You may have to pay the copayment at time of service and then submit a claim for reimbursement. See Chapter 1, "TRICARE and Medicare" for details on how Medicare Advantage works with TRICARE.

Although there is no fee to join TRICARE for Life, there is a monthly fee for Medicare Part B. The fee is about $170 in 2022, with higher fees for high-income individuals. You can sign up for Medicare 120 days <u>before</u> your 65th birthday. **There is a penalty if you delay enrollment,** so be sure to sign up on time. **You must also enroll in Medicare Part A**, but this is **free** for TRICARE beneficiaries. You do <u>not</u> need Medicare Part D. To learn more about Medicare, visit: **medicare.gov.**

Some members living internationally question why they should pay for Medicare when they are unable to use it. There are several reasons you should do so:

- First and foremost, if you are over 65, enrollment in Medicare is the <u>only</u> way to retain your lifelong TRICARE benefits. With limited exceptions, if you do not sign up for Medicare at age 65, you will not have <u>any</u> TRICARE coverage at all. See Chapter 1, "TRICARE and Medicare."

- Even though you cannot use Medicare overseas, if you enroll and visit the States, you will instantly have access to both Medicare and TFL, making health care both free and easy to use.

- If you do not enroll in Medicare at 65 and later change your mind, you will be penalized with higher monthly fees for the rest of your life. The longer you delay, the greater the penalty. Eventually, you could find TFL priced out of reach due to this penalty, leaving you with no affordable options.

Having lived overseas for many years, I am sadly aware of older vets who made short-sighted decisions that affected their lifelong coverage. Typically, these stories originate with the same question: *"Why should I enroll in Medicare when I can't use it overseas?"* They opt out, lose their TRICARE coverage, and later find it too expensive to buy back in. As they age, this leaves them with no affordable health care options in their chosen country.

Stories like this come to light when such individuals become sick or injured with no way to pay for the care they so desperately need. Their friends end up launching online fund-raisers, but it rarely ends well. These tragic circumstances will not happen if you simply pay for Medicare when eligible and maintain your life-long coverage.

You might find yourself unable to get care at an MTF once you are in TRICARE for Life. Each MTF sets its own policy of who they will see, and some will not see retirees or those on TFL. You can try to enroll in TRICARE Plus, which is an add-on plan that provides access to primary care at your MTF. Read the section below for details on TRICARE Plus.

Expert tip: Your DoD ID card may expire the month before your 65th birthday. Plan to renew the card prior to expiration to avoid any problems accessing care. Some international providers use this ID as proof of insurance, and they will balk if there is an expired date. Be aware that **there may be two expiration dates on the card.** The date on the front is the expiration of the card itself. The smaller date on the back shows when you must transition to TFL. If either of these dates have passed, it could cause difficulty with certain providers.

Types of Medicare Providers

There are three types of Medicare providers within the United States and U.S. territories. Your cost under TFL, if any, is dependent upon the type of provider you see.

- **Medicare participating providers** agree to accept Medicare's allowed amount as payment in full. These providers bill directly to Medicare so that beneficiaries will not have to submit a claim.

- **Medicare non-participating providers** may charge up to 15 percent above Medicare's allowed amount. TRICARE covers this additional fee, so TFL members should have no out-of-pocket costs. Many such providers will submit claims, so beneficiaries won't have to. This is a question that you should ask when choosing a provider.

- **Opt-Out providers** do not participate in Medicare and, by law, are not allowed to bill Medicare. TRICARE will pay its normal 20 percent share, leaving the patient responsible for the remaining 80 percent. In regions where access to medical care is limited, TFL may waive second-payer status and pay the claim as primary payer, thereby reducing your costs, but you should confirm this in advance of receiving care from an opt-out provider.

  With opt-out providers, beneficiaries must pay the bill in full and then submit a claim to TRICARE to receive the 20 percent reimbursed. The remaining 80 percent will not be reimbursed.

As of this writing, over 90 percent of primary care doctors in the United States accept Medicare, but not all are taking new patients. In most stateside locations, it is not difficult to find providers who will accept Medicare. If you enroll in a Medicare Advantage plan, however, you will be limited only to doctors within that Advantage network, possibly making it more difficult to make an appointment. Read the section entitled "TRICARE and Medicare" in Chapter 1 for more information about Medicare Advantage and Medicare supplements.

Who is Eligible for TRICARE for Life (TFL)?

- All TRICARE beneficiaries who are age 65 and above.
- TRICARE beneficiaries under age 65 who are Medicare-eligible due to a qualifying medical condition.

Note 1: Those <u>under</u> age 65, who are entitled to Medicare Part A and have Medicare Part B, are <u>not</u> required to disenroll from TRICARE Prime or the US Family Health Plan. TRICARE Prime will waive the individual Prime enrollment fee.

- Whether you keep TRICARE Prime or use TFL, your claims won't process through the regional contractor.

- Providers will file your claims with Medicare.

- Medicare will process pay their portion and then forward the claim to the TFL contractor.

- The TFL contractor will pay the TRICARE portion which should cover Medicare deductibles and copayments. The patient's share should be zero.

In such cases, if you choose not to enroll in TRICARE Prime or USFHP, you will automatically be covered by TFL.

Note 2: Some TRICARE beneficiaries over age 65 do <u>not</u> qualify for Medicare, such as a foreign spouse who has not met the residence requirement for Medicare eligibility.

- **To gain TFL benefits,** these members <u>still</u> must pay for Medicare Part B starting at 65 and will qualify under their spouse's eligibility.

- Contact your regional contractor for details <u>prior</u> to reaching age 65 so that the transition can continue without loss of benefits.

Note 3: There are exceptions to the penalty being assessed if you enroll in Medicare after age 65.

- Anyone over 65 who has an employer-provided health plan. The plan must meet certain minimum standards, so check with Medicare or your regional contractor to see if this applies to you. In this case, you would be covered only by the employer plan and will not have TRICARE coverage until you join Medicare.

- Any ADSM or ADFM over 65 does not need to enroll in Medicare until the sponsor separates from military. They will not be penalized for late enrollment in Medicare and can remain on TRICARE Prime or Select until the military sponsor separates/retires.

TFL Limitations & Exceptions

- You cannot enroll in <u>any</u> TRICARE plan if you are eligible for Medicare but do not enroll in Parts A and B. See the exceptions to this in the three notes above.

- Medicare enrollment is not needed if the sponsor is still on active duty. See note 3 above.

TRICARE Retired Reserve

Overview

TRICARE Retired Reserve (TRR) is a **premium-based, non-managed care plan** available worldwide for retirement-eligible members of the Selected Reserve and their families prior to drawing retired pay at age 60.

TRR provides comprehensive health care from retirement from the reserves until age 60. When the sponsor turns 60, the sponsor and all family members will migrate to plans available to other retiree families.

Who is eligible for TRR?

- Retired Reserve members under age 60 who are qualified for non-regular retirement and are not eligible for the Federal Employees Health Benefits (FEHB) program.

- Family members of qualified Retired Reserve members.

- Surviving spouses who have not remarried and surviving children if the sponsor was covered by TRR at the time of death. Survivor eligibility remains until the date the deceased sponsor would have turned 60 years old.

TRICARE Around the World

Limitations

- When the sponsor reaches age 60 and becomes eligible for retired pay, all family members will transition to other plans – such as TRICARE Prime or Select – subject to qualification criteria of those other plans.

- Surviving family of deceased sponsors will not be eligible if their sponsor was not enrolled in TRR at their time of death.

TRICARE Reserve Select

Overview

TRICARE Reserve Select (TRS) is a **fee-based, non-managed care** plan available worldwide for qualified members of the Selected Reserve and their families.

Who is eligible?

- Members of the Selected Reserve not on active duty orders who are not covered under TAMP and are not eligible for FEHB.
- Family members of qualifying TRS members.
- Survivors of Retired Reserve members if the sponsor was covered by TRS at the time of death. Surviving spouses cannot be remarried.

Limitations

- Members of the Individual Ready Reserve including Navy Reserve Voluntary Training Units do not qualify for TRS.
- Surviving family members are not eligible if their sponsor was not enrolled in TRS at time of death.
- Surviving spouses are not eligible if they have remarried.

TRICARE Plus

Overview

TRICARE Plus is an **add-on to non-managed care plans**, offering limited coverage at participating military hospitals and clinics. There is no cost for TRICARE Plus because it provides care only at the Military Treatment Facility (MTF) for which you have been pre-approved. Each MTF decides whether TRICARE Plus will be offered, based on their patient capacity and other considerations.

TRICARE Plus has several significant drawbacks:

- Enrollment is only for the MTF in which you are accepted.

- It provides priority access only to the primary care clinic of your approved MTF. There is no priority access for specialty care.

- TRICARE Plus does not cover <u>any</u> care from civilian providers. Unless you have other health coverage, you will be responsible for the entire bill for care received off base.

For these reasons, **TRICARE Plus is not a suitable plan for full family protection.** It should be used only to augment other coverage that you may have, such as Select or TFL.

TRICARE Plus can be a useful addition to any non-managed care you might have. For instance, if you are in TRICARE Select or TRICARE for Life and also enroll in TRICARE Plus, then you could be seen on base for routine care at no charge and still have coverage for specialists off base through your other plan. This can work both overseas and in the United States, if your local MTF participates in TRICARE Plus.

Who is eligible for TRICARE Plus?

- Anyone who is TRICARE-eligible and NOT enrolled in a TRICARE Prime plan, U.S. Family Health Plan, or a Medicare Health Maintenance Organization (HMO).

- For a dependent parent or parent-in-law, TRICARE Plus is the only TRICARE plan in which they can enroll. See Chapter 2 for more information about dependent parents and their eligibility for TRICARE.

Limitations

- The decision to offer Plus at any specific MTF rests with local commanders. TRICARE and MHS are not involved in this decision.

- You must inquire at the desired facility to be accepted into Plus. It is not transferrable to any other MTF.

- TRICARE Plus should be only an adjunct to supplement another plan, not in lieu of other coverage. It cannot be used off base and does not include priority access to specialty care within the MTF.

TRICARE Young Adult
(Prime Option)

Overview

TRICARE Young Adult-Prime (TYA-P) is a **premium-based, managed-care plan** for adult children of sponsors who lose their "regular" coverage at age 21 or 23. TYA-P works the same as TRICARE Prime. Beneficiaries have a PCM who will refer a patient to specialists when needed. Qualifying members can remain on this plan until age 26.

Beneficiaries who live in areas where the U.S. Family Health Plan is offered can enroll in USFHP instead if they wish.

Who is eligible?

- Children of active duty sponsors in all U.S. locations and overseas (if command-sponsored).
- Children of retired sponsors in Prime Service Areas in the United States.
- Eligibility begins at age 21, or age 23 if enrolled full time in an accredited institution of higher learning. Eligibility ends at age 26.

Limitations

- Dependent children remain on Prime or Select to age 21 (or to age 23 if enrolled full time at an accredited institution of higher learning, and the sponsor provides more than 50 percent of financial support).
- Enrollment is not automatic. There are specific steps to take to sign up. Enroll at least 30 days before expiration of other TRICARE plan to avoid a break in coverage.
- Cannot enroll if the young adult child is eligible for an employer-sponsored health plan based on their own employment, even if they decline the employer plan.
- Cannot be otherwise eligible for TRICARE coverage through any other means.
- Adult child must be unmarried.
- TYA enrollees are not eligible for FEDVIP vision and dental plans.

TRICARE Young Adult
(Select Option)

Overview

TRICARE Young Adult-Select (TYA-S) is a **premium-based, non-managed care plan** for adult children of sponsors after eligibility for "regular" coverage ends at age 21 or age 23. TYA-S works the same as TRICARE Select.

TRICARE Around the World

- Visit any TRICARE authorized provider. (See Chapter 5 for a discussion of authorized providers.)
- If you see a network provider, you often will pay less out-of-pocket costs, and the provider will file claims for you.
- You do not need a referral for any type of care, but some services may require pre-authorization.

Who is eligible?

- Unmarried, adult children of eligible sponsors
- Eligibility begins at age 21, or age 23 if enrolled full time in an accredited college. Eligibility ends at age 26.

Limitations

- Dependent children remain on Prime or Select to age 21, or 23 if enrolled in a full course of study at an accredited institution of higher learning and the sponsor provides more than 50 percent of financial support.
- Enrollment is not automatic. There are specific steps to take to sign up. Enroll at least 30 days before expiration of other TRICARE plans to avoid a break in coverage.
- Cannot enroll if eligible for an employer-sponsored health plan based on their own employment, even if they decline the employer plan.
- Cannot be otherwise eligible for TRICARE coverage through any other means.
- Adult child must be unmarried.

Direct Care Only

Direct Care Only (DCO) is not a TRICARE plan. **It is a status assigned to TRICARE-eligible beneficiaries who are not enrolled in a plan.** No one should intentionally be in a DCO status. You are placed there when you have not selected a plan or failed to make recurring payments for fees or premiums.

Those in a DCO status can receive care ONLY at an MTF, on a space-available basis. Since many MTFs will not serve retirees or ADFMs not assigned to that MTF, they may decline to see you. DCO also will NOT cover any care received off base from civilian providers. In short, you might have NO treatment options with TRICARE if you are in a DCO status.

If you have not used TRICARE for many years and are not sure which plan you are in, it is possible you are in a DCO status without knowing it. In our social media groups, we have learned of three situations in which this has happened to TRICARE members:

- Beneficiaries who were enrolled in TRICARE Standard in 2018 when that plan was discontinued and who failed to enroll in a new plan.

- Retirees in TRICARE Select in 2021 when a new fee was implemented. Those who did not sign up to pay the new fee were removed from Select after a grace period and placed into a DCO status.

- Those in TRICARE Select who had been paying the monthly fee and reached their catastrophic cap in any given year. Billing of the fee stops when the annual cap is reached and might not have resumed the following year. Members in this situation find themselves unenrolled from Select if billing did not restart, even though they previously had been paying the fee.

If you are in this situation, contact your regional contractor <u>immediately</u> to discuss your options. At the very least, you will be able to sign up for a plan during the annual enrollment window in November/December. Your regional contractor can advise you if there are other opportunities to sign up. See the section in Chapter 3 on "Open Season and QLEs" for details about signing up for a new plan.

Continued Health Care Benefit Program

Overview

CHCBP is a **premium-based, non-managed care** plan that:

- Provides temporary coverage for those who lose TRICARE eligibility.
- Acts as a bridge between military health benefits and any new civilian health plan.
- Provides the same coverage as TRICARE Select.
- Offers temporary essential coverage required by the Affordable Care Act.

Qualifying members can purchase CHCBP within 60 days of the loss of TRICARE eligibility. Learn more about this at **tricare.mil/Plans/SpecialPrograms/CHCBP**.

Who is eligible?

Certain beneficiaries can enroll in CHCBP when they lose TRICARE eligibility. The following shows the categories of eligible members and their length of coverage under CHCBP:

- **ADSM, released from active duty:** Up to 18 months
- **Full-time National Guard, separating from full-time status:** Up to 18 months
- **Member who is losing TAMP coverage:** Up to 18 months (See the following section regarding TAMP.)
- **Selected Reserve member losing TRS coverage:** Up to 18 months
- **Retired Reserve member losing TRR coverage before age 60**: Up to 18 months
- **Dependent child or spouse losing TRICARE coverage:** Up to 36 months
- **Former spouse who has not remarried losing TRICARE coverage:** Up to 36 months

CHCBP Limitations

- **If CHCBP coverage is due to separation from the military,** the characterization of the separation must be "honorable" or "general." Any separation that is adverse in nature would disqualify family members from CHCBP.

- **Qualified beneficiaries must sign up within 60 days of losing previous TRICARE eligibility.**

Transitional Assistance Management Program

The Transitional Assistance Management Program (TAMP) is not a TRICARE plan, but rather an assistance program for some beneficiaries when the sponsor leaves military service. For those eligible, it provides 180 days of premium-free transitional health care benefits after regular TRICARE benefits end.

Who is eligible?

Sponsors and eligible family members may be covered by TAMP if the sponsor is:

- Involuntarily separating from active duty under honorable conditions including:

  o Members who receive a voluntary separation incentive (VSI).

  o Members who receive voluntary separation pay and are not entitled to retired or retainer pay upon separation.

- A National Guard or Reserve member separating from a period of more than 30 consecutive days of active duty in a preplanned mission or in support of a contingency operation.

- Separating from active duty following involuntary retention (stop-loss) in support of a contingency operation.

- Separating from active duty following a voluntary agreement to stay on active duty for less than one year in support of a contingency operation.

- Receiving a sole survivorship discharge.

- Separating from regular active duty and agreeing to become a member of the Selected Reserve of a Reserve Component. **To qualify, the service member must become a Selected Reservist the day immediately following release** from regular active duty service.

For those who qualify, the 180-day TAMP period begins upon the sponsor's separation. During this interval, sponsors and family members are eligible to use one of the following health plan options in addition to military hospitals and clinics:

- TRICARE Prime or Prime Overseas (where available).

- TRICARE Select (U.S. and internationally).

- U.S. Family Health Plan (in designated locations).

Other active duty programs such as the Extended Care Health Option (ECHO) are also available during the TAMP period. (See Chapter 4, "Special Needs/ECHO Program.")

Special Programs

There are several special MHS programs that are limited by geographic location, duration, scope of care, or eligibility. Some of these are pilot projects for potential future offerings, or they address specialized needs. Visit this page to learn more about each program: **tricare.mil/Plans/SpecialPrograms**.

Special programs may be withdrawn at any time with little prior notice. As of March 2022, the current special programs are:

- Autism Care Demonstration

- Buckley Prime Service Area Pilot — Colorado

- Cancer Clinical Trials

- Childbirth and Breastfeeding Support Demonstration

- TRICARE Prime Pilot Demonstration – Atlanta
- Chiropractic Health Care Program
- Combat-Related Special Compensation Travel Benefit
- Computer/Electronic Accommodations Program
- Continued Health Care Benefit Program
- Extended Care Health Option
- Low Back Pain and Physical Therapy Demonstration
- TRICARE Select Navigator
- Women, Infants and Children (WIC) Overseas Program

Additionally, TRICARE plans offer provisional coverage for specialized treatment. Effective dates can change at any time, but as of this writing includes:

- **Ablative Fractional Laser** for treatment of scars from burns or other trauma. Effective through 23 Feb 2026.
- **3-D Mammography** available annually for women over 40, or those over 30 with certain risk factors. Effective through 31 Dec 2024.
- **Platelet Rich Plasma (PRP) Injections** for treatment of certain elbow and knee impairments. Effective through 30 Sep 2024.

For further information on provisional coverage, visit **tricare.mil/Plans/SpecialPrograms/ProvisionalCoverage** or call your regional contractor.

The **Sexual Trauma Intensive Outpatient Program Pilot terminated on August 31, 2021.** Those dealing with the emotional issues of trauma and abuse can seek care via the mental health care benefits of your TRICARE plan.

7
TRICARE Costs

TRICARE HAS DETAILED COST SCHEDULES for all types of care. Information in this chapter is accurate as of March 2022 but is subject to change at any time. Costs are rounded to the nearest dollar. Look up current costs with the Cost Compare Tool.

Cost Compare Tool

One of the most useful features of the TRICARE website is the Cost Compare Tool, which creates a table of costs tailored specifically for you. To find it, click "Costs" at the top of the TRICARE homepage. Choose which plan you are in and your sponsor status to see a full cost breakdown. You can even compare two plans side-by-side to help in deciding which plan is best for you and your family. Refer to this often!

Cost Overview

As a guide to calculating the total cost of your TRICARE plan, please review these notes:

- In the tables below, **Prime Plans** include TRICARE Prime, Prime Remote, TYA-Prime, and USFHP.
- **TRICARE Select** includes TYA-Select.
- The cost of **TRICARE for Life** depends on whether it is used inside or outside of the U.S. and territories.
  - **If used <u>inside</u> the U.S. or U.S. territories**, Medicare is first payer. Medicare will pay its portion and then forward any unpaid amount to TFL. Your out-of-pockets costs will normally be zero.

- o **If TFL is used <u>outside</u> the U.S. and territories**, then your costs are identical to TRICARE Select, except that TFL has a lower catastrophic cap for retirees than TRICARE Select.

- **Use Parts 1, 2, and 3** of this chapter for a complete picture of your costs.
  - o **Part 1:** Premiums, fees, deductible, and catastrophic cap
  - o **Part 2:** Copayment and cost-share (also called "out-of-pocket costs")
  - o **Part 3:** Pharmacy costs

An understanding of the following terms and concepts is necessary to fully understand TRICARE costs. If you are unclear of any terms, please review the listed references.

- **Basic cost definitions** are provided in Chapter 1.
- **The different types of TRICARE providers** (network, participating, etc.) are explained in Chapter 5.
- **The Point of Service option** is described in Chapter 6 under "TRICARE Prime."
- **Group A** refers to sponsors and family members for whom military service began prior to January 1, 2018.
- **Group B** consists of sponsors and family members with initial date of military service of January 1, 2018, or later.

Expert tip: You must **spend and claim** your deductible amount before TRICARE cost-sharing begins. If you don't submit claims, you will never fulfill your deductible. Many TRICARE beneficiaries fail to submit claims "because it's not worth it" and then complain that their deductible never goes away, possibly losing thousands of dollars each year.

Part 1:
Premiums, Fees, Deductibles and Caps

For fee-based plans, the deductible and monthly fees count towards the catastrophic cap. For premium-based plans, the premiums do NOT count towards the cap.

Active Duty Service Members (ADSM)

For ADSM, medical costs should always be zero. If you do have to pay out-of-pocket costs for any reason, save your receipts and hospital/medical report, and submit a claim to your regional contractor for full reimbursement at your earliest opportunity.

Active Duty Family Members, Group A

- **Annual fee:** $0 for all plans
- **Deductible:**
  o   Prime Plans: $0
  o   TRICARE Select, E-1 to E-4: $50 pp; $100 pf
  o   TRICARE Select, E-5 & above: $150 pp; $300 pf
- **Catastrophic Cap:** $1,000 pf for all plans

pp = per person; pf = per family

Note: Additional cost-shares and deductibles apply to ADFM if using Point of Service. POS costs do not count towards the cap.

Active Duty Family Members, Group B

- **Annual fee:** $0 for all plans
- **Deductible:**
  o   Prime Plans: $0
  o   TRICARE Select E-1 to E-4: $56 pp; $112 pf
  o   TRICARE Select E-5 & above: $168 pp; $336 pf
- **Catastrophic Cap:** $1,120 pf for all plans

pp = per person; pf = per family

Note: Additional cost-shares and deductibles apply to ADFM if using Point of Service. POS costs do not count towards the cap.

Retirees and Their Family Members, Group A

- **Annual fee:**
  - Prime: $323 pp; $647 pf
  - TRICARE Select: $158 pp; $317 pf
  - TRICARE For Life (TFL): $0 (must enroll in Medicare Part B)
- **Deductible:**
  - Prime: $0
  - TRICARE Select/TFL: $150 pp; $300 pf
- **Catastrophic Cap:**
  - Prime: $3,000 pf
  - TRICARE Select: $3,706 pf
  - TRICARE For Life (TFL): $3,000 pf

pp = per person; pf = per family

Notes: Annual fees for Prime and Select count towards the Catastrophic Cap. (See note below regarding POS option.)

Retirees and Their Family Members, Group B

- **Annual fee:**
  - Prime: $392 pp; $784 pf
  - TRICARE Select: $504 pp; $1,008 pf
- **Deductible:**
  - Prime: $0
  - TRICARE Select network: $168 pp; $336 pf
  - TRICARE Select non-network: $336 pp; $672 pf
- **Catastrophic Cap:** All plans: $3,921 pf

pp = per person; pf = per family

Note: Additional cost-shares and deductibles apply if using the TRICARE Prime **Point of Service (POS) option.** Annual fees for Prime and Select count towards the annual Catastrophic Cap.

TRICARE Reserve Select

- **Monthly fee:** $47 pp; $230 max pf
- **Deductible:**
  - E1-E4: $56 pp; $112 pf
  - E-5 and above: $168 pp; $336 pf
- **Catastrophic Cap:** $1,120 pf

pp = per person; pf = per family

TRICARE Retired Reserve

- **Monthly premium:** $502 pp; $1,207 max pf
- **Deductible (network provider):**
  - Network: $168 pp; $336 pf
  - Non-network: $336 pp; $672 pf
- **Catastrophic Cap:** $3,921 pf

pp = per person; pf = per family

TRICARE Young Adult (Active Duty sponsor)

- **Monthly premium:** TYA-P: $512; TYA-S: $265
- **Deductible (sponsor E-4 & below):**
  - TYA-P: $0
  - TYA-S, sponsor E-1 to E-4: $56 pp; $112 pf
  - TYA-S, sponsor E-5 & above: $168 pp; $336 pf
- **Catastrophic Cap:** All plans: $1,120

P = Prime; S = Select; pp = per person; pf = per family

Note: If members in TYP-Prime use **Point of Service option,** additional cost-shares and deductibles apply.

TRICARE Young Adult (Retiree sponsor)

- **Monthly premium:** TYA-P: $512; TYA-S: $265
- **Deductible (in-network):**
  - TYA-P: $0
  - TYA-S: $168 pp; $336 pf

- **Deductible (non-network):**
  - TYA-P: $0
  - TYA-S: $336 pp; $672 pf
- **Annual Catastrophic Cap:** All plans: $3,921

P = Prime; S = Select; pp = per person; pf = per family

Part 2:
Copayments and Cost-Shares

Copayments and cost-shares are known as "out-of-pocket costs." Look up your plan and the sponsor's status below.

Expert tip: Estimating your out-of-pocket costs before you submit your claim will help later when the claim is adjudicated. Since you will know in advance what to expect, it allows you to easily determine if the claim was settled correctly. Your analysis also gives you the details you need if you later dispute the claim.

TRICARE Prime

ADSM, ADFM & Transitional Survivors:
- $0 for all covered services

All Other Prime Beneficiaries (in-network):
- Preventive care: $0
- Primary care: $22
- Specialty care: $33
- Urgent care: $33
- Emergency services: $67
- Inpatient: $168 per admission

TRICARE Prime Point-of-Service Option (POS)

If a Prime enrollee obtains routine care without a doctor's referral, this is known as Point-of-Service. It is subject to a POS deductible of $300 per person or $600 per family, <u>plus</u> a 50% cost-share of remaining expenses. POS costs do NOT count towards the Catastrophic Cap, so **there is no upper limit on how much you might pay!** This can be hugely expensive, so **always get a referral for routine care** if you are in any Prime plan.

TRICARE Select

ADFM (in-network):
- Preventive care: $0
- Primary care: Group A $24; Group B $16
- Specialty care: Group A $38; Group B $28
- Urgent care: Group A $24; Group B $22
- Emergency room: Group A $99; Group B $44
- Inpatient, Group A: $21 per day
- Inpatient, Group B: $67 per admission

ADFM (non-network):
- Preventive care: $0
- Inpatient/maternity, Group A: $21 per day
- Inpatient/maternity, Group B: 20% of allowable charges
- Other TRICARE-covered inpatient expenses: 20% of allowable charges

TRICARE Select for Retirees Group A:
- Preventive care: $0
- Primary care: $32 network; 25% non-network
- Specialty care: $50 network; 25% non-network
- Urgent care: $32 network; 25% non-network
- Emergency room visit: $133; 25% non-network
- Inpatient care (network): 25% of hospital charges up to $250/day + 20% of separately-billed charges
- Inpatient care (non-network): 25% of hospital charges up to $1,053/day + 25% of separately-billed charges

TRR & TRICARE Select for Retirees Group B:
- Preventive care: $0
- Primary care: $28 network; 25% non-network

- Specialty care: $44 network; 25% non-network
- Urgent care: $44 network; 25% non-network
- Emergency room visit: $89 network; 25% non-network
- Inpatient care (network): $196 per admission
- Inpatient care (non-network): 25%

TRICARE Reserve Select:
- Preventive care: $0
- Primary care: $18 network; 20% non-network
- Specialty care: $28 network; 20% non-network
- Urgent care: $22 network; 20% non-network
- Emergency room visit: $44 network; 20% non-network
- Inpatient care (network): $67 per admission network
- Inpatient care (non-network): 20%

Part 3:
<u>Pharmacy Costs</u>

Pharmacy costs for 2022 are shown below. For beneficiaries other than ADSMs, **select brand-name medications taken for long-term conditions may only be filled twice at retail pharmacies** and then must be filled via home delivery or at a military pharmacy. For more info, visit **www.tricare.mil/coveredservices/pharmacy**.

<u>**Military Pharmacy:**</u> No charge for any medications

<u>**Home delivery, 90-day supply:**</u>
- Generic: $12
- Brand Name: $34
- Non-formulary: $68

<u>**Network Retail Pharmacy, 30-day supply:**</u>
- Generic: $14 (maximum)
- Brand Name: $38
- Non-formulary: $68

Non-Network Pharmacy (U.S. and U.S. territories):

- **TRICARE Prime plans:** 50% cost-share after the Point-of-Service deductible is met. For ADSM/ADFM on Prime or Prime Remote, contact your regional contractor if non-network pharmacy is your only alternative.

- **ADFM on Select and all TRS members:** 20% cost-share after deductible is met.

- **Retirees, TRR members and all others in Select:** 25% cost-share after deductible is met.

- **All other plans**:
  - **Formulary:** $38 or 20% of the total cost, whichever is more, after meeting your deductible.
  - **Non-formulary:** $68 or 20% of cost, whichever is more, after meeting your deductible.

There is a higher copay for non-formulary drugs. For details, visit **tricare.mil/CoveredServices/Pharmacy**.

Continued Health Care Benefit Program:

All CHCBP costs shown are valid through 31 December 2022. Paygrade refers to the sponsor's rank before separation.

CBHBP Premium per quarter:
$1,654 pp; $4,079 pf
(pp = per person; pf = per family)

CBHBP Annual deductible:
AD/Guard/Reserve, E-1 to E-4: $56 pp; $112 pf
AD/Guard/Reserve, E-5 & above: $168 pp; $336 pf
Retired (network): $168 pp; $336 pf
Retired (non-network): $336 pp; $672 pf
(pp = per person; pf = per family)

CBHBP Catastrophic Cap:
Active Duty: $1,120
Retiree: $3,921

CBHBP (Active Duty)

Preventive care: $0
Primary care: Network $16; non-network 20%
Specialty care: Network $28; non-network 20%
Urgent care: Network $22; non-network 20%
Emergency room visit: Network $44; non-network 20%
Inpatient, per admission: Network $67; non-network 20%

CBHBP (Retiree)

Preventive care: $0
Primary care: Network $28; non-network 25%
Specialty care: Network $44; non-network 25%
Urgent care: Network $44; non-network 25%
Emergency room visit: Network $89; non-network 25%
Inpatient: Network $196 per admission; non-network 25%

Vision & Dental Costs

Breakdown of vision and dental costs is too complex to reflect here due to the variety of options.

- Active duty families and reservists can find dental costs at **tricare.mil/Costs/DentalCosts/TDP/Premiums**. To view all costs, be sure to click on Premiums, Cost Shares, and Plan Maximums in the navigation menu.

- Retiree dental plans can be purchased through FEDVIP, which is separate from TRICARE. There are a variety of plans offered by different contractors.

- Vision care for ADFM and retiree families is also available through FEDVIP.

- Visit **www.benefeds.com** for FEDVIP vision and dental plans. Each one has a downloadable PDF with a full table of cost and benefits.

8
TRICARE in the Philippines

THE PHILIPPINES IS THE ONLY COUNTRY in the world that has its own set of rules for TRICARE. Specialized resources are available to help you use your health benefits and file claims.

- TRICARE Overseas has a page solely dedicated to using TRICARE in the Philippines. To learn more, visit **www.tricare-overseas.com/beneficiaries/philippines**.

- In our popular Facebook group **"TRICARE in the Philippines"**, you can chat with others who live or travel in the Philippines. Find this page by visiting **www.theTRICAREguy.com**.

- The only VA clinic outside the United States is in Manila, near the embassy. This outpatient clinic supports veterans with qualifying service-connected conditions. See **benefits.va.gov/manila/** for more details.

- There are volunteers throughout the Philippines to help retirees, family members, and survivors navigate their TRICARE and VA benefits. See "Resources and Contact Information" at the end of this chapter to find these dedicated volunteers.

While this chapter provides helpful tips for using TRICARE in the Philippines, **please read the entire book!** The other chapters are critically important and provide crucial information about your health care benefits, how to file claims properly so that you can be reimbursed quickly, and much more.

Certified and Preferred Providers

A key feature of TRICARE in the Philippines is the use of **"certified" and "preferred" providers.** These designations are used only in the Philippines. "Preferred" is roughly equivalent to a TRICARE network provider. "Certified" equates to a non-network provider. You should visit <u>only</u> preferred or certified providers in the Philippines, except in a medical emergency. The following definitions apply:

- **Preferred Providers** will bill TRICARE directly for medical care. Patients will pay only their deductible and copayment and will not have to submit a claim. The vast majority of preferred providers are located around Metro Manila, Subic, and Clark/Angeles City. There are very few elsewhere in the country.

- **Certified Providers** normally will not file claims for you. The beneficiary must pay the bill in full and then submit a claim to TRICARE Overseas for reimbursement.

- All other providers in the Philippines are NOT approved for use except for emergency care. **In a medical emergency, call an ambulance or visit the nearest emergency room without delay.** TRICARE will reimburse the expense.

TRICARE Philippine Provider Search Tool

TRICARE Overseas provides an online tool to find certified and preferred providers in the Philippines. For anyone planning to use TRICARE in the Philippines, it is essential to become skilled in using this tool. We have seen far too many people relying on word-of-mouth about where to go, and then having trouble with their claim because they went to an unauthorized provider. Learn to search for yourself, and do not depend on others to tell you what providers to use. The list of Philippine providers changes <u>often</u>.

To find the search tool, visit the TRICARE Philippines site at **www.tricare-overseas.com/beneficiaries/philippines**. Scroll down and click "Search now."

Always use this tool when seeking care in the Philippines. Just because a provider was on the list last year doesn't mean that they still are. A provider recommended by a friend may no longer be on the list, causing your claim to be denied. Always double check!

Using the Philippine Provider Search Tool is a bit of an art. Here are some proven tips for getting the best possible results. **Read these tips carefully** and follow them **precisely**.

- **The Provider Search Tool does NOT work well on a smartphone.** A pop-up page appears, which is hard to see on a phone, and prevents you from viewing your search results. Use this search tool **only** on a computer.

- **If searching outside of major urban areas, enter only the name of your province.** Do NOT fill in any of the other boxes (e.g., the name of the town, hospital, or clinic) or you may get no results at all.

- **If you are in the Clark/Subic/Metro Manila area**, however, you can enter the name of the town to narrow down your results.

- If you don't get satisfactory results in your province, try a neighboring province if it is just a short drive away.

- When you click "Search", a pop-up window appears with an X in the top right corner. **Do NOT click the "X"! If you do, the window will close, and you will not get your search results.** Instead, scroll to the bottom of the pop-up and click "Show My Results." You will then see your list of providers.

- For providers with multiple locations, be aware that not every location may be certified or preferred. **Carefully check the address of any provider** that you find to ensure that it is the one that you want. If you go to an unauthorized location, your claim might be denied.

In our Facebook group, people often claim that there are no Preferred or Certified providers near them. **This has proven to be wrong 100% of the time!** Every province has providers; most have dozens. People do not find providers near them because they are not using the search tool correctly. **The three most common mistakes are:**

- Using the search page on a smartphone, not a computer.
- Entering the name of your town.
- Clicking the "X" to close the pop-up window instead of scrolling to the bottom and clicking "Show My Results."

If you avoid these mistakes, you should be able to find providers near you. Join our Facebook group for further advice and support.

If you are in a situation where there is no certified or preferred provider within a reasonable distance – for instance, if you must rely on ferry service – call TRICARE Overseas for authorization to use a non-certified provider for routine care. **Ask them to send the authorization in writing via the secure messaging portal.** If questions arise later, having this written authorization will be a tremendous help to you.

Professional Fees

Professional fees are a feature of the Philippine health care system where doctors and other professionals bill separately for the cost of their services. **TRICARE will reimburse these professional fees**, but it takes particular care and additional documentation.

You should include an itemized list of professional fees with your Philippines claim. **The doctor or hospital may prepare this list, or you can create it by yourself.** If you prepare it yourself, it should be typed and printed from your computer, <u>not</u> handwritten.

To claim professional fees:

- Some of our group members have said that a **Current Professional Terminology (CPT) code is needed for any procedure performed**, but this appears to be inconsistently enforced. We recommend including the CPT code to avoid problems. You can look up codes at **www.aapc.com/codes/cpt-codes-range**.

- **For outpatient care,** list the doctor's name, specialty, what care was provided, CPT code, and the amount billed in Philippine pesos.

- **For inpatient care,** provide an itemized list organized by date. Your list will show:
  - Date of service
  - Name and specialty of doctor (e.g., surgeon, OB-GYN, anesthesiologist, etc.)
  - Description of service provided
  - CPT code
  - Billed amount, in Philippine pesos

- **For an anesthesiologist,** include the name and dosage or quantity of the anesthetic used and for how long.

- **Each medical professional who charges a fee should give you a detailed receipt** which includes the provider's name, field of specialty, medical license number, address or phone number, amount of fee, and a statement of your diagnosis or a diagnostic code. Submit these receipts with your claim.

- As with all other claims, **call the TRICARE Overseas Singapore office 24 hours <u>after</u> uploading your claim**. Ask them to review your claim, page by page. They will tell you right away if they see any problems.

If your reimbursement for care in the Philippines is less than you expected, it is likely because the professional fees were not reimbursed. *Don't give up!* Continue calling to determine the problem and resubmit your claim. You should eventually be reimbursed.

Expert Tip: If you are admitted as an inpatient at a preferred hospital, your cost-share is capped at $250 per day for hospital charges **plus** 20% of separately billed charges. If the professional fees are bundled into the hospital charges, however, they would fall within the $250 daily cap, and you may end up saving money. If professional fees are separate from the hospital bill, you will pay up to $250 per day **plus** a percentage of the professional fees. Ask if professional fees can be bundled into the hospital bill to reduce your cost-share.

Pay with Plastic

In the Philippines, the rejection rate of claims is quite high, and it is tough to fix once rejected. The best approach is to ensure that your claim is approved on the first try.

One reason for these rejections is the historically high rate of fraudulent claims in the Philippines, where the providers or beneficiaries (or both) try to defraud the U.S. government. Cash payment makes it very easy to obscure transactions, so this is a red flag for fraud. When paying with cash, you can expect that your claim will receive greater scrutiny, take longer to settle, and is perhaps more likely to be denied altogether.

The easiest way to avoid this problem is to pay with a credit or debit card. Many hospitals and clinics don't accept credit cards so **shop around within your community before a medical emergency**. This way, you will know where to go in a crisis.

There is a TRICARE rule that claims under $1,000 do not require a credit card receipt. Despite that, we recommend that you submit a receipt with **every** claim that you submit as a quick and easy way to avoid extra scrutiny. **Denied claims can take months to resolve,** often requiring multiple phone calls and resubmissions. If you get it right the first time, it is quite possible to receive your reimbursement in 3-6 weeks with little stress.

If you pay with cash, TRICARE will want a more complete paper trail. To do this, complete one of the following steps:

- Get a money order for the exact amount. Keep a copy of the money order to submit with your claim.

- Withdraw the required amount of cash from the bank just before paying your bill and keep the bank receipt.

- Pay with a direct wire transfer or online payment service to the hospital.

This added paperwork trail reduces the level of concern during the review of your claim and should help it resolve faster. For more information on acceptable documentation for your payment, go to **www.tricare.mil/proofofpayment**.

To streamline future claims, research within your community to see if there are any providers who accept credit cards. Do this BEFORE a medical emergency so you will know where to go.

Reimbursement in the Philippines

We are aware of three ways to receive your TRICARE reimbursement. Use the method that works best for you.

- **Direct deposit to a U.S. bank.** If you have a checking or savings account in the States, you can arrange for direct deposit, which reimburses your money quickly. The bank MUST have a U.S. routing number, not a BIC (Bank Identifier Code) or SWIFT code (international routing code). See Appendix A ("Establishing Direct Deposit") on how to set this up for yourself and your family members.

- **Mailed check in U.S. dollars.** If you have not set up direct deposit, then TRICARE will mail you a check. You can deposit a U.S. dollar check in the Philippines if you have a dollar account in a Philippine bank. There usually is a fee for depositing a check written in dollars, and it will take about four weeks for the check to clear before you can access your money.

- **Mailed check in Philippine pesos.** If you do not have a dollar account, TRICARE can mail a check to you in pesos. **Check "Yes" in Block 13 of your DD-2642 claim form** to indicate payment in foreign currency. Some banks may be unwilling to deposit a check from TRICARE, so this can lead to difficulties.

Expert Tip: If you live in the States and are planning to move to the Philippines, be sure to keep a U.S. bank account open to receive direct deposits from TRICARE. Otherwise, you will have to depend on checks mailed to the Philippines, which might be lost or delayed. Due to banking laws, it is difficult or impossible to open a U.S. bank account when you are physically outside the United States.

Veterans Service Organizations

There is a great deal of assistance available in the Philippines for retirees, their spouses, family members, and survivors. Knowledgeable volunteers can help with obtaining VA benefits, filling out TRICARE claims, Social Security issues, reporting the death of a veteran, and other matters related to military service.

Veterans Service Organizations (VSOs) such as Veterans of Foreign Wars (VFW), American Legion, and Disabled American Veterans (DAV) will be happy to assist. Veterans should make sure that their spouse is aware of this support so that they can get help in managing benefits. The VA maintains a list of VSOs at **www.va.gov/vso.**

There are three Retired Activities Offices (RAOs) in the Philippines, plus numerous RAO satellite offices. RAOs have official standing with the Department of Defense, ensuring that they are properly trained and managed. The main RAOs are in Manila, Subic, and Angeles City. Any of these can direct you to a satellite office in your town or province. Contact information for the three RAO main offices is in the "Resources" section later in this chapter.

Besides general assistance with VA and TRICARE benefits, RAOs offer another very important service: **access to a military mailbox to receive mail from the United States**. You can pick up your mail at an RAO or have it forwarded it to your home by courier. There is an annual membership fee to have the RAO receive your mail, plus an additional fee for courier delivery to your home. The following section describes how you can use this service to receive TRICARE prescription refills by mail in the Philippines.

Mail Delivery of Prescription Refills

One of the great things about the RAO military mail service is that TRICARE beneficiaries in the Philippines can use Express Script's home delivery service to receive prescription refills by mail. You can either pick it up at their mailroom (at the Clark, Subic, or Manila office) or arrange to have refills forwarded to your home for a fee. Express Scripts can offer a huge benefit in refill costs and convenience. The FPO is authorized to receive mail weighing up to 16 ounces, but this weight limitation is waived for prescription refills from Express Scripts and the VA.

The only problem is that **Express Scripts requires a prescription written by a U.S.-licensed doctor**. This can be hard to find in the Philippines, so you may need to establish an ongoing relationship with a doctor in the States. Ask if they will do remote consultation with you annually to renew your prescription(s). TRICARE currently allows telemedicine (remote consultation with your doctor via the internet). Many members use this method to obtain prescription renewals.

Resources & Contact Information

There are a great many resources to help with TRICARE and other military benefits. Join our Facebook group "TRICARE in the Philippines" to ask questions. We are committed to helping people understand their TRICARE benefits in all situations.

This is the contact info for the three Retired Activities Offices in the Philippines:

RAO Manila: No website available.

Hours: Mon/Weds/Fri 9:00 – 2:00
Email: manilarao2012@yahoo.com
Phone (landline): 8-255-2728
Phone (mobile): 632-8255-2729

RAO Subic: www.raosubic.com

P.O. Box 075
Olongapo City, 2200
Philippines

PSC 517 Box 5000R
FPO AP 96517-1000

Email: dir@raosubic.com or staff1@raosubic.com
Phone: 011-63-47-222-2314 or 047-603-0775

RAO Angeles: 1925mcarthur.wixsite.com/raoangeles

Retiree Activities Office
PSC 517 Box 2000R
FPO AP 96517-0021

Email: rao_ac@yahoo.com
Phone: 0915-965-0847 or 0939-847-7526

For many years there was a dedicated contractor to assist with TRICARE in the Philippines, known as Global24. You will still find Global24 listed on the TRICARE website, but today all customer support issues are handled by the TRICARE Overseas regional office in Singapore. If you call or email Global24 directly, your communication will be forwarded to the TRICARE regional office. There are a variety of ways to get in touch:

Phone: +632-8687-8656

From PLDT: 1-800-1441-0576

US (Stateside) toll-free: 1-877-678-1208
(Press Option 7 for Overseas Select)

Email: Support@GLOBAL24NS.com

Regional Office (Singapore): 65-6339-2676

The Philippines toll-free line is only available to callers with service provided by PLDT. We recommend that you use Skype for international calls. U.S. toll-free numbers are free on Skype, and Singapore is about two cents per minute.

Tips & Tricks for TRICARE in the Philippines

Over the years, members of our Facebook group, "TRICARE in the Philippines", have shared tips on getting the most from TRICARE benefits in the Philippines. The following is a selection of some of the best tips shared in our group.

- **Renew your military ID card.** It is not unusual for hospitals in the Philippines to accept your retiree ID card as proof of TRICARE insurance. If you cannot prove that you have TRICARE, you will end up paying the entire bill upfront and must submit a claim for reimbursement.

  o Your card may show two expiration dates. The first is on the front in large font. The second, on the back, is dated the month before you turn 65, which is when you must transition to TRICARE for Life. **Your TRICARE coverage is still valid even with an expired ID**, but it can be hard to prove this to a hospital in the Philippines. Obtaining an updated card ahead of time can make things much easier.

  o **Obtain a new ID card at the DEERS office at JUSMAG** in Manila (by appointment only). The ID office is in the same building as the VA clinic, **but the VA does not issue military ID cards**. If you go to the VA clinic and ask for an ID, they might give you a VA ID card, but not a military retiree ID card.

o **To cut through the red tape, contact one of the three RAOs**. They may be able to help you get an appointment at the ID/DEERS office and can help with the application form.

- **Enroll your spouse and children in DEERS.** It is essential that all family members are registered in Defense Enrollment Eligibility Reporting System (DEERS). Without that, they cannot enroll in TRICARE. Your local RAO can help, or you may need to visit the embassy. If enrolling newborns overseas, read our instructions in Chapter 2. **Be sure to keep DEERS updated** with your current mailing address, email address, and changes in your family (e.g., birth, death, marriage, divorce, etc.).

- **Sign up for PhilHealth.** PhilHealth is a national insurance plan in the Philippines. All Philippine citizens are eligible, as well as some retiree non-citizens, and those who have given up their Philippine citizenship but returned to the country. PhilHealth is considered OHI (Other Health Insurance) by TRICARE. When you use this program, you must first settle your bill with PhilHealth and get their Explanation of Benefits (EOB). Include the EOB with your TRICARE claim, and list PhilHealth as OHI on the claim form. See Chapter 11 for more information about OHI on TRICARE claims.

- **Do not include your over-the-counter (OTC) medications on TRICARE claims.** TRICARE Overseas does not cover OTC medications. If you have even one OTC on your receipt, this can cause the entire claim to be rejected. If you are shopping for both OTC drugs and prescription drugs on the same trip, pay for them separately and get separate receipts.

- **Use the TRICARE Philippine Provider Search Tool!** Do <u>not</u> ask your friends which doctors are Certified or Preferred. We repeatedly hear stories about members who were referred by friends to providers who no longer qualify, causing their claims to be denied. Even RAOs and VSOs make this mistake! Read the section in this chapter about how to use the search tool. You will save yourself a lot of time, effort, frustration, and money.

- **Have access to <u>lots</u> of cash!** Many hospitals in the Philippines **require payment in full at discharge**, and **some are cash-only. Others may require payment at <u>admission</u>** or periodically during a prolonged inpatient stay. **Hospitals have even been known to hold a patient "hostage"** until the bill is paid while continuing to run up steep daily fees. Without cash, this can be a very stressful and costly situation. Some members of our group have had to put a lien on their cars or other assets when they could not come up with the cash immediately.

- **Establish a relationship with a nearby hospital.** The admissions process for first-time patients in the Philippines can be lengthy and arduous. Before ANY medical care is provided (even emergency care), the hospital will want to collect your personal details, verify your access to cash or creditworthiness, and confirm the validity of your insurance. If you are gravely injured or ill, this wasted time can be critical. To avoid delays and be admitted quickly, visit the business office of your preferred or certified hospital BEFORE an emergency, so that the enrollment/validation process is completed <u>before</u> an emergency arises.

- **In a genuine emergency, go to the nearest emergency room.** If facing threat to life, limb, or eyesight, do not waste time searching for a preferred or certified provider. Get your emergency care without delay. TRICARE <u>will</u> accept your claim.

- **Learn to use Skype or a similar calling app.** Many of our group members avoid calling the TRICARE regional office due to the cost of international calling. With Skype, calls to the TRICARE Singapore office are about two cents per minute, and toll-free numbers to the U.S. are free. Skype can be installed on any Android phone, iPhone, Mac, or Windows computer. No cellular service is needed if you have Wi-Fi.

  Calling apps like Skype are useful for more than just calling TRICARE. You can also use them to call Social Security, DEERS, Medicare, your bank in the U.S. (if you have one), and more. Remember: U.S. toll-free numbers are FREE to call. This can be a BIG cost-savings for you!

Final tip...practice, practice, PRACTICE! The use of TRICARE is a skill that can be learned. The best time to learn is during a non-critical situation. A small claim for routine care is the perfect time to try using your benefits and see how it works. You can familiarize yourself with the process and make a mistake or two until you get it right. Reading this book is a great start, but **you will not truly understand TRICARE until you try it for yourself.**

9
Prescription Refills While Traveling

AMONG THE MORE FREQUENT health concerns of most travelers, especially those who are planning an extended vacation overseas, is how to obtain prescription refills on the road. Travelers often wonder: *Will the medications I need be available on my trip? Will TRICARE pay? How do I buy them?*

The laws in each nation are different, and not all medications used in the U.S. can be found in other countries. If a specific medication is critical to your health, you will need to carefully research the laws in your destination location(s). Two questions are vital: *"Is it legal for import?"* and *"Can it be purchased in-country?"*

An important thing for retirees to bear in mind: You and your family no longer have the SOFA (Status of Forces Agreement) protections that you once enjoyed as an active duty family. If you "slip up" and are caught with prohibited medications at the border, you are at the mercy of local authorities. The base legal officer is not going to intervene or bail you out. Take extra care to research local laws when you are carrying prescription drugs into another country.

ISOS – the TRICARE Overseas contractor – specializes in medical logistics worldwide. They may be able to advise you about your destination, even if you are enrolled with a different TRICARE contractor. There are many ways to ensure that you have the medications you need while away from home. Each of the following options are discussed in this chapter:

- Bring enough to cover your entire trip
- Visit a military pharmacy
- Refill delivery by mail (Express Scripts)
- Retail pharmacy (TRICARE reimbursable)
- Retail pharmacy (out-of-pocket cost)
- Deployment Prescription Program
- Refill through the VA

Bring Enough for Your Trip

This may seem evident, but it bears mentioning: Bring enough medications to cover your trip. Don't assume that you can drop into any drugstore for a quick refill. If you will be on a longer trip and normally order a 30-day supply from your local pharmacy, ask your doctor or pharmacist about a 60- or 90-day refill. They usually will accommodate you. (See exceptions below.)

If you have enough time before your trip, you can switch to Express Scripts home delivery which provides 90-day refills for most medications. It can take some time to make this transition, so don't attempt this change at the last minute. To learn more about home delivery, go to **militaryrx.express-scripts.com**.

There may be limits on what you can bring in and/or how much, so carefully research each country you plan to visit. Check immigration and customs websites and other official sources to learn the laws. Common things to watch for:

- **Prescriptions** must be in the <u>original</u> packaging in which they were issued and include a label with your name, dosage, and quantity.
- **Over-the-counter medications** also should be in the original packaging that clearly lists the ingredients.
- **Quantity:** Some countries limit the quantity travelers can bring in. Anything over 30 or 90 days might be deemed excessive according to local laws.

The adage "Ignorance of the law is no excuse for breaking it" means that the burden of research rests squarely on you. **Violation of import laws can result in fines, confiscation of the medication, or imprisonment.**

Some countries prohibit medications commonly used in America. In Japan, pseudoephedrine, which is common in cold and allergy medications in the United States, is prohibited. Codeine or tramadol can land you in jail in Greece or Saudi Arabia. Customs officers worldwide will be indifferent to your plight if you are found in possession of what they consider "contraband." Worse yet is when a traveler is given a chance to declare certain medications but fails to do so. The act of concealment can bring a harsher penalty than simple possession. "Research before you go" is the best advice. Do your homework!

Expert Tip: "Don't put all your eggs in one basket." When traveling, split your medications between different bags, such as checked and hand-carried bags. If one bag is lost, you will still have enough on hand while you figure out what to do. Ask your provider to issue your prescription in <u>two</u> labeled containers, each properly labeled with your name. Not all doctors will do this, so start your preparations well in advance so that you can handle any unexpected challenges.

Military Pharmacy

If, despite your best efforts, you need refills on the road, the cheapest way to obtain them is at a Military Treatment Facility (MTF). Medications obtained at an MTF are free, but there are some precautions to bear in mind:

- **Most nations of the world do not have American MTFs.** Even if they do, the drive might be too far to be worth it. Investigate this <u>before</u> your trip.

- **Many MTFs no longer serve retirees**. An MTF's priority is to serve military members and command-

145

sponsored dependents. The decision of whether to serve others is made by local commanders at each base, not by TRICARE. Don't assume that they will help.

- **Some bases may have restricted access** at the main gate due to security concerns. Even if an MTF says that it will treat retirees, it may be impossible to get on base. Access can change on very short notice due to military operations, so always have a back-up plan in mind.

- Regardless of base access, you must **confirm whether the pharmacy carries your medication** and what sort of prescription they need from your doctor. Local practices may differ from what you are used to. Don't waste vacation time on a wild goose chase that might not pay off. Call ahead to find out.

Refills by Mail

Express Scripts, the TRICARE prescription contractor, offers mail delivery of refills. However, this is not a practical solution for travelers outside the U.S. who will not have a mailing address while traveling. Express Scripts will not mail to a foreign address.

For those living overseas, this can be a workable solution if you have an FPO or APO address, but each country differs in what they allow. **In Germany, mail delivery of medications is prohibited by law, even to an APO address.** Keep in mind that other countries may have similar laws.

If you will be visiting friends overseas, don't ask to use their FPO/APO address to receive your mail! In most nations, it is a violation of military regulations for a member to use their FPO/AFO for anyone who isn't part of their household. You would put your friend at risk of losing their mail privileges or worse. This is a matter that you must solve on your own.

Check the nearest Retired Activities Office (RAO). Many overseas locations with a large population of military retirees have an RAO at the U.S. embassy, consulate, or military base. Depending on local policy, RAOs with an FPO/APO address may legitimately allow use of their post box to receive medications on behalf of local retirees. Before traveling, look for an RAO in your intended destination. In the Philippines, use of the FPO address is widely available to retirees nationwide. See Chapter 8 on how to use military mail to receive prescription refills in the Philippines.

Retail Pharmacy (Reimbursable)

The most flexible option for obtaining refills is to visit a retail pharmacy and purchase your medications locally. With a non-network pharmacy, you will pay out of pocket and submit a claim for reimbursement. At a network pharmacy, you will pay only a small copayment, but network providers are hard to find in most locations overseas.

To file a TRICARE claim, you will need a receipt with specific information printed on it. A credit card or cash register receipt alone is <u>not</u> sufficient. See Chapter 11 for details on filing a claim for prescription refills.

Pharmacies in many countries will happily sell you any number of medications without a written prescription. Use your best judgement to ensure that you are getting the genuine article, not a pirated or substandard product. "Let the buyer beware" is our best advice.

Expert tip: There are smartphone apps that help find low-cost prescription refills but, as far as we know, these apps work only in the States. GoodRX and SingleCare are two examples, but there are others. If you are buying from a network provider, you cannot use the app and get TRICARE benefits on the same refill. Compare the cost of the refill on the app vs your TRICARE copay and pick the cheapest option. If you don't have a smartphone, call local pharmacies (including those at big box stores) to ask for a price check.

Out-of-Pocket Retail Purchase

During your travels, you may find that local pharmacies can provide your medications very inexpensively even without a prescription. This is not uncommon in less-developed parts of the world. When you do this, you are not likely to get the receipt that you would need to file a TRICARE claim, so you will end up paying the cost out-of-pocket.

With this strategy, simply pay for the medication with no intention of submitting a claim. Medications can be far cheaper overseas.

Real Life Story: In Thailand, a 90-day supply of my cholesterol meds cost only $7 at my local drugstore, less than the TRICARE copay I would have paid at a hospital pharmacy. This was the cheapest alternative for me, even without filing a claim.

I was comfortable with this approach while living in Thailand because I was able to build trusted relationships with my local doctor and pharmacist. However, if you are in an unfamiliar setting, exercise caution with this method. The last thing you want is a fake medication that might do more harm than good. Make sure that you are buying from a reputable source and that the medications you obtain are genuine.

Deployment Prescription Program (DPP)

Express Scripts also offers what is known as the Deployment Prescription Program (DPP). This program allows deploying service members and contractors/government employees with TRICARE coverage to bring as much as 180 days of medication with them. You can even arrange to have refills sent to your military address around the world if this is allowed by local laws.

If so, your doctor should write a deployment prescription to cover this period. This is not for vacationers or family members, but it is a great option for those traveling on military orders. Visit the Express Script website, click the "Benefits" menu and then select "Deployment Prescription Program."

Refill through VA

As discussed earlier, many veterans on TRICARE plans are eligible for medical care from the VA, even without a service-connected disability. This can include prescription drugs and refills. (See "VA Health Care" in Chapter 1.) Refills received from the VA cost $0 or $15, depending on the veteran's priority group.

Once your prescriptions are entered into the VA health system, you can obtain your refills by mail or in person at a VA hospital or clinic within the U.S. Research which VA hospitals are in the areas where you are traveling.

Those with service-connected disabilities may be able to use the VA Foreign Medical Program (FMP) to refill prescriptions overseas. FMP provides 100 percent reimbursement, rather than the 80 percent that you would get through TRICARE. This can save you a bundle on higher-priced prescriptions. To learn more, read the section in Chapter 1 on VA Disability Benefits.

Real Life Story: Traveling with a CPAP

Travelers to Japan who wish to bring in more than 30 days' worth of medical supplies, such as syringes or a CPAP machine, must obtain a *Yakkan Shomei,* a type of import certificate. I was unaware of this some years ago and carried my CPAP in and out of Japan many times without the required documentation. This escaped the attention of customs, so I was never questioned about it. You should never depend on luck, however!

In 2021, I was traveling from Thailand to Seattle via Narita, Japan. I called ahead to Japan Airlines to ask if my CPAP was excluded from my limit of carry-on items as it is in America. After I asked this seemingly innocent question, the airline staff became deeply concerned. They called back several times and asked for photos of my CPAP along with the serial numbers and a picture of the display with the machine powered on. They asked me repeatedly if I would be using it in-flight, which I stated that I would not.

When my family and I checked in at the airport in Bangkok, JAL representatives met us at the counter, had me unpack the CPAP, double-checked the serial number, put a special tag on it, and finally allowed us to travel. For that trip, we were not even entering into Japan; it was just a layover for the next flight. We got the go-ahead, but it was a nerve-wracking experience until we got that final approval.

Please don't let my personal experience deter you from doing the right thing. Had I not declared this piece of equipment – and their team had discovered it in my luggage – it could have been a real problem. The moral of the story is this: Every country has its own perspective on medications and medical equipment. Take nothing for granted. Research and follow the laws of each country... and enjoy stress-free travels!

10

During Your Appointment

It's time to go to the doctor! Perhaps you are on a family vacation in the States, or you got sick in a foreign country. Maybe this is the very first time that you've used TRICARE away from home. In a new setting, the process may feel a bit disorienting or confusing. In this chapter, we will walk you through what to expect. Whatever the situation, it's probably very different from the days when you simply walked into a military hospital, saw the doctor, picked up your prescriptions, and walked out.

Where Should You Seek Care?

If this is a medical emergency, go to the nearest emergency room without delay. <u>No pre-authorization is needed,</u> and POS fees will not be charged. Even ambulance fees will be reimbursed if medically necessary. Whether the ER is network or non-network, give them your TRICARE information. Most U.S. ER's will coordinate with TRICARE for direct payment, even if they are not a network provider.

Some decisions about your care arise even before you get to the hospital or clinic. In every case, there will be paperwork to collect during your visit. Let's look at some common scenarios.

If you are active duty:
- You should seek care at a military hospital or clinic if this is reasonably possible.
- For emergency care, if no MTF is nearby, go immediately to the nearest civilian emergency room. No referral or

        authorization is needed. Notify your PCM as soon as practicable after receiving care.

- For urgent care, visit an MTF or call the MHS Nurse Advice Line. They will advise you on the preferred course of action.

- Routine care for active duty members should <u>always</u> be with your PCM or with a referral.

If you are in a managed-care plan like TRICARE Prime and you see your PCM first, <u>relax</u>. You will either get no bill at all, or you will be asked to pay a small copay for the office visit. Your PCM will provide any referrals you might need, and you will not have to file a claim. When you work within the system, the process is quite simple.

If you are in a managed-care plan and get routine care <u>without</u> first seeing your PCM, this might be very expensive. By not seeing your PCM first, you are using the Point of Service (POS) option. With POS, you will have a large deductible and 50 percent cost-share. Worse still, it does not count towards your family's catastrophic cap, so there's no upper limit on how much you might pay. **If you are unable to see your PCM for a referral,** at least call your regional contractor. They might be able to give pre-authorization or other advice to save you some money. It is definitely worth the effort.

If you are in a non-managed care plan like Select or TRICARE for Life (TFL), there is no PCM. <u>You</u> determine which doctor to see and make your own appointments. If you are in the United States with TFL, you should make an appointment with a Medicare provider. Medicare will be first payer, TRICARE second payer, and your cost should be zero. If you are overseas and do not have other insurance, TRICARE is first payer, and you will use TFL exactly like TRICARE Select.

    If you have any questions about who to see, contact the Nurse Advice Line at **mhsnurseadviceline.com**, available

24/7/365. They can point you in the right direction and might be able to arrange an appointment for you. To learn more about this valuable resource, see "MHS Nurse Advice Line" in Chapter 12.

There are many places – particularly overseas – where non-network providers will be your <u>only</u> option. **When you use a non-network provider, be prepared to:**

- Pay the <u>entire</u> bill before checking out (see Payment Tips later in this chapter)
- Collect all required paperwork (see next section).
- Submit a claim (see Chapter 11).

What Paperwork to Collect for Your Claim

Before an appointment, you need to know what paperwork to collect during your medical visit. This will expedite your claim and might save you a trip back to gather what you need. **These documents do NOT need to be in English.** International SOS, the TRICARE Overseas contractor, has robust translation capabilities. Translation might slow the processing of your claim by a few days, but it is not an obstacle. From my own experience, I have submitted receipts in Thai and Japanese with no discernable delay.

There are three items to collect during your visit to use later in your claim: A medical certificate, an itemized receipt, and a cash register or credit card receipt.

The medical certificate (also called a "medical report" or "hospital report") provides a description in clinical terms of why you were seen, your diagnosis, any lab tests conducted, treatment provided, and medications that were prescribed. It also may include diagnosis codes for your condition and the circumstances of your care (e.g., injury, acute illness, follow-up appointment, preventive care, etc.). This document must include your name, the doctor's name and medical license number, plus the name, address, and phone number of the hospital or clinic. It is not a receipt and will have no cost information.

It is best to request the medical report/certificate at check-in. This ensures that the report/certificate is prepared during your consultation. If you request it at check-out, your doctor will have moved on to the next patient, and you will have to wait until the doctor has the time to prepare it. You can save a lot of time by mentioning it upfront.

Some hospitals or clinics might charge you a small fee for creating the medical report/certificate. Have them add the fee to the total bill; it will be reimbursed in your claim.

The second item to collect is an itemized receipt. This lists, in some detail, lab tests that were conducted, the doctor and nurse fees, hospital fee (if any), and all medications and supplies provided annotated with the cost of each item. The itemized receipt **must be pre-printed with the hospital or clinic's name and address or phone number**. They can write all the other information by hand, but computer-printed is always best. **The itemized receipt should have a "Paid" stamp on it, or some other indication that you paid the bill.**

The third item to collect is a cash register or credit card receipt. This is a simple receipt of the total amount billed, amount paid, and zero balance remaining. It is not itemized. Ideally, you will pay with a credit or debit card, to avoid the scrutiny of a cash transaction. Official TRICARE guidance says that you do not need a receipt for claims under $1,000, but I ignore that rule and <u>always</u> include a receipt with each claim, big or small. Of my 24 most recent claims submitted, all were approved on the first try. Don't take shortcuts! Do everything you can to ensure your claim is approved the first time around.

Manage Your Care

We will not repeat generic advice about being prepared to ask questions during your appointment or assessing risk for any medical procedures. Tips for being an informed patient hold true regardless of who your insurer is. However, as a consumer, you should be prepared to address issues of importance to your TRICARE coverage. There is no blanket checklist on this subject; it comes with experience and through participation in our online forum while learning from the experiences of other members.

Here are some examples from our Facebook groups of how members managed their care within TRICARE:

- One member was told by his regional contractor that TRICARE would not cover the cost of an EKG during his annual physical without a statement of medical necessity. I had the opposite experience: my EKG was accepted without a referral. You never know, so **be prepared to ask for referrals to back up your claim.**

- TRICARE will cover the cost of COVID testing if it is requested by your doctor and if an FDA-approved test is used. The COVID tests that many countries use are <u>not</u> FDA-approved. Be sure to discuss this with your doctor.

- In 2020, I was hospitalized for an intestinal issue. I wanted a COVID test because I had recently been in a high-risk area. After I explained the circumstances, my doctor wrote up an order for the COVID test. It was reimbursed by TRICARE because of the doctor's order.

- For inpatient care, TRICARE covers the cost of a semi-private room. If you upgrade the room, TRICARE will not cover the additional cost. In many Thai hospitals, there are no shared rooms; even the most basic rooms are private. To avoid confusion, I made sure this was not mentioned in the paperwork. The invoice simply said, "Standard room", and my costs were covered.

TRICARE Around the World

Over time, you will learn which questions to ask that are unique to your situation. If you need professional advice, call the MHS Nurse Advice Line, your regional contractor, or the nearest TRICARE Support Center if you are overseas. Chapter 12 has more information about these resources.

Payment Tips

The following payment tips can save you money and make it easier to get your claim approved. These are things that you should consider before the day of your appointment.

In Chapter 8, we discussed the pitfalls of paying with cash. **Cash payments can be a red flag to claims reviewers,** even though there is nothing wrong with cash payment. In many places around the world, cash is the only accepted form of payment. Consider any of the steps below to create a precise record and avoid questions on your claim:

- **Withdraw the needed cash from a bank or ATM** and include the bank/ATM receipt with your claim.

- **Get a cashier's check for the exact amount of your bill** and submit a copy with your claim.

- **If you have a bank account in-country, pay via direct bank transfer,** and print a receipt.

- **Use an international payment service** like Wise to directly pay the provider from your U.S. bank account. This gives the paper trail you need for your claim.

TRICARE says that you do not need a receipt for bills under $1,000, but we include a receipt for EVERY claim regardless of cost. It's easy to do and avoids problems later. While the above tips may seem over-the-top, they have been proven to make the claims process run more smoothly if you are in an area known for high rates of fraud. Keep copies of everything in case there are questions later. You can learn more about proof of payment at **www.tricare.mil/proofofpayment**.

If you are paying internationally with a credit card, it is increasingly common for vendors to give you a choice of billing in U.S. dollars or local currency (e.g., euros, pesos, yen, etc.). **Always opt to pay in <u>local</u> currency, <u>not</u> in U.S. dollars.** When a foreign vendor processes the payment in dollars, they will give you a poor exchange rate to boost their profit margin. If you choose to bill in local currency, then your credit card issuer or bank will do the currency conversion, giving you a better rate. I have seen differences of up to $50 on charges of $600. That's an astonishing 8 percent premium just to have the vendor calculate the currency exchange!

Some members in our Facebook group swear that they lose money every time TRICARE converts foreign currency to U.S. dollars on a claim. Personally, I haven't noticed this. What I find is that if prevailing exchange rates improve while TRICARE is processing your claim, you might receive a few extra dollars. If rates drop during that time, you may end up a few dollars short, but I have not seen a tendency one way or another. We mention it here in case it's something that you want to pay attention to.

Before going abroad, obtain a credit card that charges no international fee. Most credit and debit cards charge a fee of one to three percent for all international transactions. However, many cards are available without these fees if you shop around. If you have a **rewards card,** you can get cash or points back for your medical expenses. Instead of paying up to 3 percent in fees, you could be earning cash back on all your medical expenses!

Below is a summary of my personal financial considerations for paying overseas with a credit card:

- I file my claims immediately after each appointment, so reimbursement normally arrives before the credit card bill is due. This allows me to use the reimbursement to pay off the card without incurring any finance charge.

- I pay zero international fees by choosing the right credit card. Most cards add 1% to 3% for purchases overseas; by shopping around, you can find a card with no such fees.

- My card gives at least 1% back on medical expenses. Some cards offer even more but watch out for annual fees!

- I decline the vendor's offer to bill in U.S. dollars, saving up to 8% on the expense. This practice borders on a scam because it takes advantage of the unwitting consumer, and the costs are not disclosed. This conversion rate scheme is becoming more and more common worldwide, particularly in areas frequented by tourists.

- The conversion rate "scam" is increasingly seen at foreign ATMs, which offer to convert your cash withdrawal to U.S. dollars before sending the transaction to your bank. ALWAYS decline this conversion and have the ATM process your transaction in <u>local</u> currency. Your bank will give you a better exchange rate.

Expert Tip: Many overseas ATMs do the same "currency exchange trick" described above. While dispensing cash in the local foreign currency, they offer to do the calculation in U.S. dollars. They have a number of ways of disguising this with highly confusing terminology. **JUST SAY NO!** Have the ATM calculate the withdrawal in the local currency, and your bank will convert to dollars. Withdrawing the equivalent of $600 at a time can easily cost you an additional $50 by having the local bank do the currency conversion.

11

Prepare and Submit Your Claim

THROUGHOUT THIS BOOK, we have presented many valuable benefits of your TRICARE health plan. Despite this, many people feel compelled to purchase additional insurance to be covered fully. Others do not bother to file their TRICARE claims, leaving significant money on the table. With little effort on your part, TRICARE will cover medical expenses for you and your family. This is the "how-to" chapter where you will learn to prepare and submit claims so that you can put that money back in your pocket.

A Vicious Cycle: Why People Don't File Claims

Our unique vantage point of the global TRICARE community through the stories shared in our Facebook group allows us to see trends and issues faced by beneficiaries worldwide. One of the most frustrating things that we hear regularly is the litany of excuses for not filing claims: *"It's too hard"* or *"It's only a few dollars"* or *"Why bother? They'll probably reject the claim anyway."*

We've seen this pessimistic view play out repeatedly, so let's expose the fallacy. Say, for example, that you have an annual deductible of $150. This means your TRICARE benefits don't kick in until <u>after</u> you have a total of $150 in medical expenses for the year. But just having the expense is not enough – you must file a claim, so that TRICARE can credit it against your deductible. In other words, **you must file that first claim knowing that you might get nothing back.** This is why so many people say: *"Why bother?"*

This flawed logic overlooks one important fact: **If you don't submit the claim, you will <u>never</u> fulfill your deductible**, and you can go the entire year without getting ANY medical expenses reimbursed. Eventually, you may say in frustration: *"It's too late now! I should have started sooner."* You've got a shoebox full of crumpled receipts and are no closer to grasping how the system works than you were at the beginning of the year.

This is not hypothetical. Members in our group confess to this exact behavior for years on end, leaving <u>thousands</u> of dollars on the table that could instead be in their bank accounts. That's money they could be using for groceries, college, car payments, travel, savings, and more.

In a similar scenario, many beneficiaries simply don't understand deductibles. They file a claim and, to their great puzzlement, get nothing back. Lamenting that "TRICARE doesn't work," they give up without realizing that the first claim fulfilled their deductible and that the next one would result in cash reimbursement. This is why we emphasize basic vocabulary in our online community and in this book. When people don't grasp the meaning of terms like "deductible" and "catastrophic cap", they end up making costly mistakes.

As for the argument *"It's too hard"* – that's only true if you haven't the time to learn how to file a claim or find network providers. It might seem confusing at first, but after you do it two or three times, you'll see that it's not so difficult, and you will understand the process better. The only hard part is educating yourself – ***and you have the guidebook in your hands!*** Yes, there is learning curve, just like any worthwhile skill – but with practice, all your excuses will vanish.

Your medical requirements may be minimal while you are relatively young and healthy, but the clock is ticking; we all age. One day you might need bypass surgery. Your spouse will unexpectedly require chemotherapy. Your child will get hurt falling off a bike. These things come without warning, which is why you should learn – *today* – how to use your TRICARE benefits. You don't want to be frantically trying to figure this out during a family crisis.

It's heartbreaking to see people struggle because they did not learn to use their TRICARE benefits when they had more time. And what if it's <u>you</u> in ICU, rather than your spouse? Will your husband or wife have to figure this out alone? You are doing your family a disservice by <u>not</u> building this skill under more relaxed circumstances and sharing what you learn with your spouse.

You have made it this far into the book – <u>this</u> is the money chapter. No more *"It doesn't matter"* or *"It's not worth it."* Get past that. Follow our guidelines and file your first claim.

Who Do You File With?

A few simple rules determine where to file your claim:

- **If you are enrolled in TRICARE Overseas,** file your claim with TRICARE Overseas even if you receive care while visiting the States.

- **If you receive care <u>outside</u> the United States and U.S. territories,** file the claim with TRICARE Overseas, no matter where you live.

- **If you live in the United States or U.S. territories and receive care <u>inside</u> the United States or U.S. territories,** file the claim with your home region. For instance, if you live in the East region and receive care in the West region, file with TRICARE East.

- **If you are on Medicare/TFL and receive care <u>inside</u> the United States,** you normally will not need to file a claim. If you do, however, file with Wisconsin Physician Services (WPS), the TFL contractor.

- **If you are on TFL and obtain care <u>outside</u> the United States,** file your claim with TRICARE Overseas.

It is important to file with the right contractor. If you submit your claim to the wrong one, they won't forward it or tell you to refile with the right contractor. They will go into a full 60-day deliberative process and then reject your claim for cryptic reasons. You won't understand <u>why</u> the claim is denied, even though it looks like you did everything right. It can take several calls to straighten it out and start all over again – and that's only if you ask the right questions. In this type of situation, people often give up in frustration, eat the cost, and tell everyone that TRICARE doesn't work – all because they don't understand what went wrong.

This isn't just negative talk. We've seen this exact process play out over and over again with members in our group. It is always puzzling when claims are rejected because there are so many variables to consider; it can take some digging to figure out the problem. When there is a lot of money at stake, this can be quite stressful, causing a nominal three-week approval process to stretch out for months...or never get reimbursed at all.

How do you avoid all this stress and angst? By submitting a high-quality claim that gets approved the first time through, without going into that cycle of rejection. The rest of this chapter – and our One-Stop Checklist in Appendix D – focuses on how exactly how this is done.

How to File: Fax, Mail, or Online

There are various ways to file your claim, depending on your contractor: fax, mail, or online. **When you are filing claims with TRICARE East or West**, plan on mailing it in since they do not offer an online option.

When filing claims with TRICARE Overseas, you can mail it or file online. We <u>strongly</u> recommend that you file claims online at the TRICARE Overseas web portal for reasons that we will explain later.

No matter which method you choose, **you can receive your reimbursement by direct deposit** to your U.S. savings or checking account. Funds will arrive about three business days after approval of your claim. If you haven't arranged for direct deposit, they will mail you a check, which can take weeks to arrive... or possibly get lost in the mail. If you are planning to move overseas, make sure to keep your U.S. bank account open. It is extremely difficult – perhaps even impossible – to open U.S. bank accounts when outside the United States.

When to File

There are time limits for filing TRICARE claims:

- **For care received <u>inside</u> the United States or U.S. territories,** you have 12 months to file a claim.
- **For care received <u>overseas</u>,** you have 36 months.

If you have Other Health Insurance (OHI), you must file with the OHI <u>first</u> and wait for it to settle. Your OHI will issue an Explanation of Benefits (EOB); attach that to your TRICARE claim and specify the OHI in Block 11 of the claim form. Remember, OHI itself will take a while to settle, so don't wait until the last minute if OHI is involved. Delay in resolving OHI is <u>not</u> an excuse for missing your TRICARE filing deadline. **If your claim is returned to you for additional information, you MUST respond within 90 days** or by the original filing deadline – whichever is later – or the claim will be denied.

Some people prefer to save up their claims and submit them all at once. We recommend that you file claims as soon as possible after you receive care. The longer you wait, the harder it becomes to complete the task. Paperwork disappears, you forget important details about your care, or you get overwhelmed as multiple claims start to pile up.

With a laptop and a scanning app on your smartphone, you can even create and submit claims from your hotel room while traveling. In a truly paperless process, I routinely scan receipts and other documents with my phone, mark-up the PDFs on my computer, sign electronically, and upload everything through the contractor's portal. By the time I get home from traveling, my claims are done – all without a printer or flatbed scanner.

Assemble Your Documents

Now it's time to assemble your documents into a claim package, which will include some – or all – of the following:

- TRICARE claim form (DD-2642)
- Hospital or doctor's report (also called a "medical certificate")
- Itemized receipt, marked "Paid"
- Cash register receipt
- Bank/ATM cash receipt (if paying by cash). This is especially important in the Philippines.
- Explanation of Benefits (EOB) if you have OHI
- In the Philippines, details of professional fees. (See Chapter 8 to learn more about this.)
- Any other documentation to substantiate your claim.

It is acceptable for documents to be in a foreign language. ISOS, the TRICARE Overseas contractor, has robust translation capabilities.

Complete Your Documents

Appendix D provides our unique "One-Stop Checklist" to prepare your claim, compiled from a variety of official sources. If you follow our checklist carefully, you can expect your claim to sail through the approval process in just a few weeks.

- In the top margin of the DD-2642 claim form, neatly write or type **"Beneficiary paid provider directly."** This cues the contractor to send reimbursement to you, not to the provider. Sometimes reimbursements are sent incorrectly to the provider even though the beneficiary (you!) has already paid the bill in full. As unfair as it sounds, the regional contractor will refuse to pay you until the money is clawed back from the provider, which can take up to a year or more. Make sure that they understand that the money is supposed to come to <u>you</u>! Mention this in your follow-up call as well.

- **At the top of ALL other pages, write the patient's name and the sponsor's SSN or DBN** (DoD Benefit Number). The DBN is an 11-digit number on the back of your military ID card. It can be used in lieu of an SSN as a protection against identity theft.

- Download the DD-2642 claim form from your regional contractor's website. Fill it out on your computer or print it and complete by hand. Printing a stack of these forms in advance will allow you to file by mail even without access to a printer, such as when you are traveling.

- Check the appropriate box in Block 7 if your medical condition is work- or accident-related. The government may try to recover cost of your care if a third party was involved. See the section at the end of this chapter on "Third Party Liability." **Failure to disclose this may be viewed as insurance fraud.**

- If you have OHI, you cannot submit a TRICARE claim until the OHI has settled. In Block 11, fill in the information about your OHI (if any) and attach the EOB. **Failure to disclose OHI may be considered insurance fraud.**

- In Block 8a, describe <u>why</u> you were seen. Be clinical and descriptive. There is not much room, so keep it focused: "Sustained high fever", "Abdominal pain", "Monitoring of kidney function as recommended by physician." This is where the claims adjuster will look if there is no diagnosis code on the medical report, so be <u>precise</u>. If you need to elaborate on the circumstances of an injury or other details, attach a page, and mention this page in block 8a.

- **Keep copies of <u>everything</u>!** Vital documents can get lost enroute or misplaced during processing. Protect yourself by taking the time to make copies.

Filing by Mail

If you are mailing your claim, be sure to use the correct address. Mailing addresses are subject to change, so double-check at **tricare.mil/ContactUs/ClaimsAddresses**.

TRICARE East
TRICARE East Region Claims
ATTN: New Claims
P.O. Box 7981
Madison, WI 53707-7981

TRICARE West
TRICARE West Region Claims
P.O. Box 202112
Florence, SC 29502-2112

TRICARE Overseas (Active Duty claims)
TRICARE Active Duty Claims
P.O. Box 7968
Madison, WI 53707-7968

TRICARE Overseas - Africa & Eurasia (non-AD)
TRICARE Overseas Program
P.O. Box 8976
Madison, WI 53708-8976

TRICARE Overseas – Asia-Pacific, Latin America, Canada (non-AD)
TRICARE Overseas Program
P.O. Box 7985
Madison, WI 53707-7985

TRICARE for Life (U.S. & Territories)
WPS TRICARE for Life
P.O. Box 7890
Madison, WI 53707-7890

TRICARE for Life (all overseas regions)
Use the overseas claims addresses above.

Pharmacy claims (U.S. & Territories only)
Express Scripts, Inc.
P.O. Box 52132
Phoenix, AZ 85072-2132

Continued Health Care Benefit Program
TRICARE East Region Claims
CHCBP Claims
P.O. Box 7981
Madison, WI 53707-7891

Claims for NOAA Members (all locations)
U.S. Department of Commerce
Office of the General Counsel
Office of the Assistant General Counsel for Finance and
    Litigation General
Litigation Division
1401 Constitution Ave NW Room 5890
Washington, DC 20230-0001

Filing by Fax

The TRICARE Overseas Program (TOP) and TRICARE Dental Program (TDP) are the only programs that promote filing claims by fax. It can take up to <u>two weeks</u> to import a faxed claim into the claims processing system, whereas submission via the TOP online portal puts your claim into the processing system within 24 hours. If speed of processing is important to you, you should learn to file via the TOP online portal.

TRICARE Around the World

The following fax numbers are available for submitting claims:

TRICARE Overseas fax: 1-608-301-2251

TRICARE Dental Program fax:

U.S. & U.S. Territories: 717-635-4565

International claims: 844-827-9926 or 717-635-4520

We recommend calling <u>before</u> you send a fax to ensure that you have the right number. Next, call <u>after</u> sending your claim to confirm that ALL the pages were received and are legible and correct. See our "Follow Up" section below.

Filing Online

With TRICARE Overseas, you have the option of submitting your claim via their web portal. One of the greatest advantages to this is speed: your claim is imported into their processing system within one business day. This differs from fax or mail, where it can take weeks for your claim to be entered into the processing system.

It takes a bit of computer literacy to master the portal. At a minimum, you'll need to know how to scan, merge documents, and upload files via the contractor's website. If you don't have such skills, find someone who can teach you or assist with the process. Be sure to work only with trustworthy people since you may disclose personal information like Social Security or bank account numbers, leaving you vulnerable to identity theft. See Chapter 12 for sources of local assistance.

Besides the benefit of faster reimbursement, another advantage of online filing is that you can find and fix any problems early in the process. Read "Follow Up" below about how to conduct a telephone review of your claim, and to instantly resolve any problems that are found BEFORE your claim enters the formal review process.

Follow Up: How to Avoid Claim Rejections

If I had to pick just <u>one thing</u> to make the TRICARE Overseas claim process go smoothly, it would be this: **After submitting your claim online, call them the next business day (after waiting a minimum of 24 hours).** A customer support representative will review your claim over the phone. If they find a problem, it can be fixed during the call or by sending more documentation via the portal. Earlier I wrote that I have never had a claim rejected. That does not mean I always get it perfect on the first try. What it means is that I call the next business day and immediately fix any problems they find. With this one step I generally get reimbursed within 21 days, but some take longer.

When you call, you need to ask:

1. Did you receive my claim?
2. What pages do you see? *(Compare this to your copies to confirm that everything is there.)*
3. Are all pages legible? *(Pages sometimes become garbled in online submissions.)*
4. Do you see any problems?
5. Lastly, confirm that the payment will be sent to <u>you</u>, not to the health care provider.

These steps can prevent your claim from going into a rejection cycle. It seems to take eight weeks or more to reject a claim, and then you receive a cryptic notice such as: "Requested information not provided." This doesn't mean that they asked for something that you failed to provide (since we've never seen them ask for anything during the claims process). It means that your initial submission was deficient for some reason, and it is up to you to figure out what went wrong.

I am a big fan of TRICARE and want everyone to have as positive an experience as I have had. The best thing to do is to not let a claim go into that rejection cycle in the first place. To

169

achieve this, make that follow-up call and fix any problems at the very start of the process. Don't wait eight-plus weeks for a rejection, only to have to start all over again. **Follow our One-Stop Checklist** in Appendix D, wait at least 24 hours, and then make that follow-up call. *You can do this!*

Fixing Problems with Your Claim

When you call after submitting your claim, what do you do if a problem is found? In most cases, you will not have to redo the entire claim; simply submit any additional documentation that is requested. This can be a very quick process via the contractor's portal, even if you did not originally submit your claim through the portal. Each contractor has a Messaging Center where you can submit documents. **When you call, be sure to get the claim number and include it in your message with the new documents.**

With TRICARE Overseas, if you submit your claim via the online portal, you will find a confirmation message with your claim number in the Messaging Center. Click "reply" on the confirmation message, attach any new documents requested, and send. The documents will be added to your claim package.

As you did with the original claim package, wait 24 hours, and then call to make sure the additional documents were received, are legible, and have been added to your claim. If they see no further problems, you can be 99% sure that your claim will be quickly paid as long as it was for a covered condition.

Pharmacy Claims

Pharmacy claims are similar to other TRICARE claims. Use the same claim form, DD-2642, and check "Pharmacy" in Box 8b.

There are specific requirements for a pharmacy receipt:

- **Items that must be typed or computer printed on the pharmacy receipt include the following:**

pharmacy name, date the prescription was filled, drug name and dosage, quantity provided, and the amount paid by the beneficiary.

- **Items that can be handwritten on the receipt include:** the prescription number, pharmacy address, doctor's name, pharmacist's signature, retail price, and the amount paid by other health insurance (OHI).

In the United States or U.S. territories, mail your pharmacy claim to Express Scripts at:

Express Scripts, Inc.
P.O. Box 52132
Phoenix AZ 85072-2132

For international pharmacy claims, use the applicable address for overseas claims in the "Filing By Mail" section earlier in this chapter.

Dental Claims

Forms and information about filing TRICARE dental claims can be found at **tricare.mil/FormsClaims/Claims/Dental.**

For the Active Duty Dental Program, send the claim form and supporting documentation to:

United Concordia
Claims Processing
P.O. Box 69429
Harrisburg, PA 17106-9429

For the TRICARE Dental Program (U.S. & territories), mail or fax your claim to:

United Concordia
TRICARE Dental Program
P.O. Box 69451
Harrisburg, PA 17106
Fax: 717-635-4565

For the TRICARE Dental Program (International), mail or fax your claim form to:

United Concordia
TRICARE Dental Program
P.O. Box 69452
Harrisburg, PA 17106
Fax: 844-827-9926 (toll-free) or 717-635-4520

For FEDVIP dental plans, visit the website of your dental administrator for information on how to file claims.

Filing Complaints

Despite your best efforts, there is always a chance that something will go wrong. Perhaps a claim is denied or approved for a lesser amount than expected. Maybe you didn't receive the professional and courteous treatment that you deserve. What happens next?

The first thing you should do is **pick up the phone and call!** Nine times out of ten, the issue can be resolved over the phone. They will either explain what went wrong and give you a chance to fix it, or they may convincingly explain why your claim is denied, and you will understand that an appeal will not help. Several times, my reimbursement was less than expected. After discussing it by phone, they recognized their mistake and sent the remaining money. I didn't have to submit anything more.

If you are unable to resolve the matter by phone, you might be able to **find an advocate** who can help. Such advocates include:

- **Ombudsman or patient advocate** at hospitals, clinics, and other care centers. Their role is to help patients resolve issues within a facility when they arise.

- **Beneficiary Counseling and Assistance Coordinator (BCAC)** whose role is to help with questions about TRICARE eligibility, enrollment, referrals/authorizations, and claims.

Learn more about advocates and other sources of assistance in Chapter 12.

If after all of this, you are still at an impasse, then it's time to submit a formal complaint. In TRICARE, there are two kinds:

- **Appeal:** If you were denied care or payment to which you believe that you are entitled.

- **Grievance:** If you are not satisfied with the quality of care received, the behavior of any specific person in the TRICARE system, or any other non-appealable issue.

Appeals are broken down into four types:

- **Factual appeal** is when you are denied payment for services or supplies that you received.

- **Medical necessity appeal** is when you are denied authorization for care or services because TRICARE feels it isn't medically necessary.

- **Pharmacy appeal** is when you don't agree with a decision about your pharmacy benefit.

- **Medicare-TRICARE appeal** applies if you're eligible for both TRICARE and Medicare, and Medicare denies your services or supplies. This would not apply to an overseas claim since Medicare cannot be used overseas.

Examples of grievances include:

- **The quality of care** given by a provider, such as inappropriate care, not enough care, or poor results.

- **The attitude or behavior** of providers and their staff.

- **Incorrect information** provided to you.

- **Delays or errors** in processing authorizations.

- **Patient safety issues** at a facility.

- **Privacy concerns.**

Submit grievances and appeals to the contractor who is handling your claim. Each regional contractor has its own forms and procedures for complaints. Search for "complaint" using the search function on your regional contractor's website. It will lead you to their guidance for submitting a complaint.

Expert tip: If you plan to call your regional contractor with a question, do <u>not</u> message them before calling. This could backfire. TRICARE Overseas – and perhaps the others – are allowed a full 30 days to answer your written question. If you call during that 30-day period, they will say: *"You've already written to us about this. Give us 30 days to reply,"* and they will not answer your question over the phone. It's infuriating! I've learned to **call without messaging first**. Once I have an answer, I ask them to send a response through the Secure Messaging Center, so I have the answer in writing.

Third Party Liability

Under federal law, the government has the right to recover the cost of care if treatment was due to the intentional or accidental actions of another. Recovery of costs may be from the third party or from the TRICARE beneficiary if their care was reimbursed by insurance of either party. This right of cost-recovery applies even if the care was provided at an MTF.

Chapter 10, Section 5 of the TRICARE Operations Manual 6010.56-M, "Claims Adjustments and Recoupments" says:

The Federal Medical Care Recovery Act (FMCRA) provides for the recovery of the costs of medical care furnished by the United States to a person suffering a disease or injury caused by the action or negligence of some third person. Under this act, the United States has a right to recover the reasonable value of the care and treatment from the person(s) responsible for the injury. For TRICARE beneficiaries, this includes care that may be received by the beneficiary at a Uniformed Services facility or under TRICARE, or both. The FMCRA applies only to illness or injury (including work-related injuries) caused by a third party, either intentionally or negligently, or injuries caused by a third party's failure to act when a duty to act could be implied.

If TRICARE suspects your condition involves third-party liability, they will send you DD Form 2527, "Statement of Personal Injury – Possible Third Party Liability Form." This can be triggered by the diagnostic codes used by your health care provider. The International Classification of Disease (ICD) codes specify not only the illness or injury to a patient but also how the injury occurred (e.g., sports injury, auto accident, etc.). Or the diagnosis might be ambiguous with no clear reason specified. In these cases, the TRICARE Regional Contractor will send you DD Form 2527 to clarify the circumstances. Your claim will be placed on hold until you respond and <u>canceled</u> within 35 days if you fail to respond at all.

Ask your provider to explain which ICD code is used for your diagnosis. Work with them to clarify that the injury was not due to an accident, and no third party was involved. If this can be done, you may avoid this additional step in the processing of your claim.

Additional Help & Contact Info

THERE ARE A NUMEROUS RESOURCES to help you find a doctor, navigate your health care, and submit claims. Take advantage of the many free services that are available to you. There is no need to figure it out alone or reinvent the wheel.

The TRICARE Website

The official TRICARE website is **www.tricare.mil**. You do not need to log in or create an account to use the many valuable tools on this page. One downside is that the website has so much information that it's like trying to drink from a firehose – there is no continuity, and it's hard to take it all in. The goal of this book is to organize and streamline the vast amount of information and make it more useable in real-life situations.

The tools that I have found most helpful on the TRICARE website are:

- **The Plan Finder Tool.** At the top of the TRICARE page, click "Plans." Through a series of questions, this tool will identify the TRICARE plans available to you and your family. Click "Compare Plans" in the left menu bar to compare multiple plans side-by-side. In Chapter 3, the section on the Plan Finder Tool walks you through this process.

- **The Benefits Tool.** At the top of the TRICARE page, click "What's Covered." This tool offers a keyword search to see which benefits are covered or excluded and how to use them. The section "What is Covered" in Chapter 4 gives tips on using this tool to its best advantage.

- **The Cost Compare Tool.** At the top of the TRICARE page, click "Costs." Like the Plan Finder Tool, this tool asks a short series of questions to determine your status, then presents a table of costs for you and your family. You can compare two plans side-by-side as an aid in choosing the right plan for you and your family. Keep in mind that different family members can be on different plans. This tool is discussed in Chapter 7.

By mastering these three tools, you will be able to find answers to most common questions about TRICARE benefits.

Regional Contractor Web Portals

Web portals of the regional contractors (East, West, and Overseas) are discussed in Appendix A. This is where you will create log-in accounts for you and your family members. In the regional portals, you can file claims, upload documents, set up direct deposit, securely message your regional contractor, manage TRICARE enrollment, and more.

Explore your portal. Create an account and look around. Each portal has slightly different features, so the best way to learn is just to spend time poking around. As you read, your understanding and confidence in using your benefits will increase.

Social Media

TRICARE has an official Facebook page. You can post your questions there, but don't expect a detailed response. This usually isn't the best way to get help for your specific needs. However, we do recommend that you follow their page to receive official TRICARE news and events in your Facebook feed.

Official TRICARE social media accounts include:

- Facebook: **www.facebook.com/TRICARE**
- Twitter: Follow **@Tricare**
- YouTube channel: **www.youtube.com/Tricare**
- LinkedIn: Search for **"Defense Health Agency"**

You also can join the helpful and welcoming community in our Facebook groups. Go to **www.theTRICAREguy.com** for links. Our family of unofficial TRICARE groups includes:

- **TRICARE® Around the World**
- **TRICARE® in Thailand**
- **TRICARE® in Germany**
- **TRICARE® in the Philippines**
- **TRICARE® for New Moms and Moms-to-be**

In these groups, you can interact with the author and ask questions of thousands of TRICARE users around the world.

MHS Nurse Advice Line

One of the greatest and perhaps least-used resources for TRICARE beneficiaries is the MHS Nurse Advice Line. This service is staffed by registered nurses in the Military Health System 24/7/365. These nurses are dedicated to helping you and your family with health questions and your TRICARE plans and benefits. Contact the MHS Nurse Advice Line 24/7 to:

- Get specific health care advice from a registered nurse based on your symptoms.
- Speak to a pediatric nurse for concerns about your child.
- Find an urgent care or emergency care facility.
- Receive recommendations for the most appropriate level of care.
- Schedule same or next day appointments if enrolled in a military hospital or clinic.

TRICARE Around the World

- Get an online "absence excuse" or "sick slip" for ADSM, subject to service command requirements.

The Advice Line is open around-the-clock, so you can call at any time to speak with a nurse by phone, video chat, or text chat via their portal at **mhsnurseadviceline.com**.

There is a link on their page to launch a chat with a nurse without logging in. However, **we recommend that you log in first** for the following reasons:

- If you are logged in, you can download a transcript of the chat session. You cannot do this otherwise.

- Logging in prior to the chat speeds up the verification of your identity. It also authorizes you to discuss any family member who is linked to your TRICARE account. If you don't log in, you will have a lengthy verification process at the start of the call.

The Advice Line has country-specific numbers for nations with a large U.S. military population. For other overseas locations, we have found it impossible to call because there is no way to work through the phone tree to connect to the right person. A work-around for international users is to initiate a chat session in the web portal and then tell the nurse that you prefer to converse by phone. The nurse will call you back at either your U.S. or foreign phone number. This is great for those who prefer a phone call rather than a text chat.

The following is a complete listing of country-specific numbers for the MHS Nurse Advice Line:

United States, Guam, Puerto Rico, Cuba, Diego Garcia: 1-800-TRICARE (874-2273)

Bahrain: 800-06432

Belgium: 0800-81933

Germany: 0800-071-3516

Greece: 00-800-4414-1013

Italy: 800-979721

Japan: Landline: 888-901-7144;
     Mobile: 0066-33-821820 or 0120-996-985

South Korea: 888-901-7144; mobile: 080-500-4011

Spain: 900-82-2740

Turkey: 00-800-44-882-5287

United Kingdom: 0800-028-3263

Universal International Freephone (from participating European nations): 00-800-4759-2330

Crisis Lines

A variety of services are available to those experiencing a crisis or mental health emergency. Those experiencing mental health issues that pose a threat to themselves or others should call 911 or go to the nearest emergency room. Treatment of this nature is a covered benefit of TRICARE. The following services offer **free and confidential** counseling around the clock. Trained advisors will provide assistance by phone or text and can direct you to local services for follow-up care.

- **The Military Crisis Line**
  www.veteranscrisisline.net
  1-800-273-8255 (press option 1); text 838255
  Provides confidential counseling to veterans, active duty members, Guard and Reservists. They are also there to advise concerned family and friends of vets.

- **The National Suicide Prevention Hotline**
  suicidepreventionlifeline.org
  1-800-273-TALK (1-800-273-8255)
  TTY: 1-800-799-4889
  24-hour suicide prevention service for anyone in suicidal crisis. You will be routed to the closest possible crisis center in your area. Calls are free and confidential.

- **Real Warriors Live Chat**
  www.realwarriors.net
  Serving military service members, veterans, Guard/ Reserve members, and concerned friends and family. Real Warriors offers trained crisis counselors and can direct you to non-medical counseling including peer support.

- **Other Resources**
  www.tricare.mil/CoveredServices/Mental/CrisisLines

Benefit and Debt Counseling

TRICARE beneficiaries have access to specialized counseling for benefits and debts related to unpaid TRICARE bills.

- **Beneficiary Counseling and Assistance Coordinators** (BCAC) educate beneficiaries and help with questions related to TRICARE eligibility, enrollment, referrals/authorizations, and claims processing.

- **Debt Collection Assistance Officers** (DCAO) assist with debt collection due to unpaid TRICARE claims. The debt must be in collections or listed on your credit report.

To search for a BCAC or DCAO by state or country, visit **tricare.mil/bcacdcao**.

TRICARE Service Centers (TSC)

TRICARE Service Centers in overseas locations are available for in-person assistance to TRICARE beneficiaries. These are found at some military bases around the world. The TSC can assist with care in a military clinic or hospital, care with a foreign provider off base, and answer questions about eligibility, enrollment, claims processing, and more.

TSCs can be found in:

- **Eurasia/Middle East:** Bahrain, Brussels, Germany, Greece, Italy, Spain, Turkey, and the United Kingdom
- **The Americas:** Guantanamo Bay and Puerto Rico
- **Pacific:** Japan, Korea, Guam

To find specific TSC locations and contact information, visit **www.tricare.mil/tsc**.

Veterans Service Offices (VSO)

Across the USA and in many locations around the world, you will find trained volunteers at Veterans Service Offices (VSO) who are committed to serving veterans, their families, and survivors of deceased service members. There are few places worldwide where support isn't available.

VSOs will assist with a great many needs, including helping members apply for benefits or decedent affairs after a veteran passes away. They can help the surviving spouse apply for Social Security, VA benefits, Medicare, TRICARE, and more. Examples of VSOs include Veterans of Foreign Wars (VFW), American Legion, Disabled American Veterans (DAV), and many others.

One way to find a nearby VSO is to ask within the military community in your local area. You probably know someone who is a member of a local chapter. You also can search Facebook or the internet for local organizations. The VA maintains a list of Veterans Service Organizations at **www.va.gov/vso/**.

Retired Activities Offices (RAO)

Retired Activities Offices (RAO) are often affiliated with a U.S. embassy, consulate or military base and provide a great number of services for the local retiree/veteran community. RAOs are staffed by trained volunteers who aid and assist retired military members, their spouses and surviving family members. In some countries, with logistical support from the embassy,

TRICARE Around the World

RAOs have access to an FPO/APO and can receive U.S. mail for retirees in the area. To find one near you, call the nearest U.S. embassy or consulate, or ask within your local community.

In the Philippines, RAOs play a very robust role in helping vets with access to the VA clinic in Manila and for offering mail forwarding service through the military postal system. Learn more about this unique service in Chapter 8 of this book.

VA Assistance Overseas

For veterans with a VA disability rating, VA offers access to medical services overseas through the Foreign Medical Program (FMP). FMP covers care for service-connected health issues, including medical treatment, durable medical equipment, and prescriptions. VA also may authorize foreign medical services for other conditions for those participating in the VA Vocational Rehabilitation Program.

Enroll in FMP well in advance of your international travels, as the approval process may be prolonged. Once registered, participants either pay out-of-pocket for overseas care and then submit a claim for reimbursement, or they may be able find providers who will bill the VA directly. Authorized expenses will be reimbursed 100 percent, but it can take up to a year. Since TRICARE reimbursement is faster, some beneficiaries prefer to use their TRICARE benefits instead, even though they would have to pay deductibles and copayments. To learn more, visit **www.va.gov/COMMUNITYCARE/programs/veterans/ fmp/index.asp**.

The VA also has Overseas Military Services Coordinators (OMSC) in select overseas locations to assist service members approaching separation and U.S. veterans living or working overseas. OMSCs will also advise the dependents or eligible family members of veterans. To locate an advisor near you, visit **www.benefits.va.gov/benefits/oms_Coordinators.asp**.

Global Resources

Official TRICARE website: www.tricare.mil

Military hospitals and clinics worldwide:
www.tricare.mil/Military-Hospitals-and-Clinics

TRICARE partner phone directory:
A complete list of phone numbers for all medical/dental
needs: **tricare.mil/ContactUs/CallUs/AllContacts**

Contact Wizard:
An online tool to guide you to the right phone number or
address for your needs. **tricare.mil/ContactUs/CallUs**

TRICARE East
Humana Military: **www.tricare-east.com**

TRICARE West
HealthNet: **www.tricare-west.com**

TRICARE Overseas
International SOS: **www.tricare-overseas.com**

TRICARE For Life (TFL)
Wisconsin Physician Services: **www.tricare4u.com**

U.S. Family Health Plan: www.usfhp.com

Active Duty Dental Program (ADDP)/TRICARE Dental
Program (TDP)
United Concordia: **secure.addp-ucci.com**

TRICARE Overseas Regional Call Centers
(open 24 hours, Monday - Friday local time)

Europe, Middle East & Africa:
44-20-8762-8384 from overseas
1-877-678-1207 from a U.S. phone

Latin American and Canada:
1-215-942-8393 from overseas
1-877-451-8659 from a U.S. phone

Puerto Rico: 1-877-867-1091

TRICARE Around the World
  Asia-Pacific:
    65-6339-2676 from overseas
    1-877-678-1208 from a U.S. phone
Australia/Oceana:
    61-2-9273-2710 from overseas
    1-877-678-1209 from a U.S. phone

Appendix A:
Regional Web Portals

THE FOLLOWING IS AN OVERVIEW of the web portals of the three Regional Contractors: TRICARE East, TRICARE West, and TRICARE Overseas. This appendix will help explain the key features of your web portal.

Overview

Web addresses of the regional portals are:

- www.tricare-east.com
- www.tricare-west.com
- www.tricare-overseas.com

Each portal is different; you will have to get accustomed to the layout of your particular one and where to find each feature. Create an account in your region's portal and just start exploring. If your family is geographically separated, you may need to use more than one regional portal.

Creating Family Member Accounts

Before any family member can create an online account, they must be enrolled in DEERS (the Defense Enrollment Eligibility Reporting System), which establishes their eligibility for TRICARE benefits. The mechanics of DEERS enrollment is beyond the scope of this book. You can contact the DEERS/ID card office at any military base for assistance or learn more at **www.dmdc.osd.mil**.

Each authorized family member should have their own account in their regional portal. You may have to call the regional contractor to set up accounts for younger children because federal law imposes strict internet privacy rules for children under age 13. If you are enrolled in TRICARE East or West, but have a TRICARE claim from overseas, you should create an online account on the TRICARE Overseas site. **You can have accounts with more than one regional site**, depending on your family's needs.

There are two ways to create an account: Either with a dedicated ID and password or with a DoD Self-Service (DS) Logon. The DS account can be used across a broad range of DoD sites. The method that you choose may depend on:

- Whether or not you have a Common Access Card (CAC).
- Whether or not you live in the States.

If you have a CAC, then you may already have a DS Logon. If you do not have a CAC and are living outside the United States, then creating a DS Logon might be difficult or impossible. In that case, you should create an account with a dedicated login name and password for the portal. Each contractor portal provides instructions for creating your account. The portals are linked to DEERS, so that they can instantly validate member eligibility.

Linking Family Member Accounts

Once each family member has their own online account, they can be linked. Linking accounts does two important things:

- It allows you, from your own account, to submit and manage claims for all family members.
- It signifies consent for you to speak with TRICARE representatives about the medical needs of adult family members.

Even if your account is linked to a family member, some claims will remain confidential due to their sensitive nature.

These claims will not be viewable from the linked account of a family member. Some examples of sensitive claims include:

- Abortion
- Alcoholism
- Drug abuse
- Pregnancy
- Venereal Disease
- Sexually Transmitted Disease
- AIDS/HIV
- Sexual assault
- Domestic violence

When a minor child turns 18, your access to their account ends, and you can no longer manage their health information. The link can be re-established after their 18th birthday but only with your child's consent.

Establishing Direct Deposit

We strongly encourage you to set up direct deposit for all family members, particularly if you live or travel overseas. **TRICARE direct deposit reimbursements can go only to U.S. banks.** If you do not set up direct deposit, a paper check will be mailed to you. **For most banks, you must physically be in the United States to open an account,** so make sure that you have a U.S. checking account <u>before</u> moving overseas.

Search for "Direct Deposit" in your portal's menu. This will bring up a list of all family members. Starting with the sponsor, enter all the required banking information. You will be able to reuse the same banking information for your <u>linked</u> family members if you want deposits to go to the same bank account. **For minor children, direct deposit authorization will expire on their 18th birthday.** They will have to re-establish their direct deposit preferences after turning 18.

Claim Status

Contractor portals have rudimentary tracking capabilities for your claims. In the TRICARE Overseas portal, you will receive instant notification in the message center if you file your claim online. If you submit your claim by fax or mail, you may not receive confirmation until the claim is fully processed and approved or denied. This can take two months.

If you want the current status of your claim, it is always best to call. Response to written messages is slow, and their written answers frequently are not particularly helpful. With a call, you can get up-to-date information within minutes. Sometimes I find that a claim gets "stuck" somewhere in the process, but if the customer support agent says that there are no problems, the claim eventually works its way through the system.

When processing is complete, you will receive an Explanation of Benefits (EOB) which provides a breakdown of the allowable costs, your copay/cost-share, covered amounts, and how much counts towards your deductible and annual catastrophic cap. TRICARE Overseas provides the EOB on a claim-by-claim basis, a few days after each claim is approved. The other regions bundle multiple claims into a monthly EOB. When a claim is approved With TRICARE East or West, it might take until the end of the following month to receive the EOB – up to 60 days.

Message Center

The Message Center provides a secure way to communicate with your Regional Contractor. If needed, you can send your documents through the Message Center to support a claim. Make sure to include the claim number on your documents so that each one can be attached to the appropriate claim.

TRICARE Overseas generally takes about 2 weeks to answer written questions sent through the Message Center, but their responses are often vague and non-committal. For this reason, we generally prefer to call. However, we have found a certain

Catch-22 with messaging. TRICARE Overseas has 30 days to respond to a written inquiry. If you send a message and then call to follow up, they may say, *"We have 30 days to answer your message. Call back after the 30 days if you don't hear from us."* This is very frustrating and, yes, this has happened to me. For this reason, I almost never submit questions via written message since it prevents me from getting an answer by phone for a full 30 days.

Appendix B:
Acronyms

ACA – Affordable Care Act

ACS – American Citizen Services

ADDP – Active Duty Dental Program

ADFM – Active Duty Family Member

ADSM – Active Duty Service Member

APO/FPO – Army Post Office/Fleet Post Office

BCAC – Beneficiary Counseling and Assistance Coordinator

CAC – Common Access Card

CDC – Centers for Disease Control and Prevention

CHAMPUS – Civilian Health and Medical Program of the Uniformed Services

CHCBP – Continued Health Care Benefit Program

CHAMPVA – Civilian Health and Medical Program of the Department of Veterans Affairs

CMAC – CHAMPUS Maximum Allowable Charge

CONUS – Continental United States

CPAP – Continuous Positive Airway Pressure

CPT – Current Professional Terminology

CRBA – Consular Report of Birth Abroad

DAV – Disabled American Veterans

DBN – DoD Benefit Number

DCAO – Debt Collection Assistance Officer

DCO – Direct Care Only

DEERS – Defense Enrollment Eligibility Reporting System

DME – Durable Medical Equipment

DoD – Department of Defense

DPP – Deployment Prescription Program

DS – Department of Defense Self-Service

DVA – Department of Veterans Affairs

ECHO – Extended Care Health Option

EFMP – Exceptional Family Member Program

EOB – Explanation of Benefits

ETP – Exception to Policy

FEDVIP – Federal Employees Dental and Vision Insurance Program

FEHB – Federal Employees Health Benefits

FHP – Family Health Plan

FMP – Foreign Medical Program

HIPAA – Health Insurance Portability and Accountability Act

HP&DP – Health Promotion and Disease Prevention

ICD – International Classification of Disease

ISOS – International SOS

JUSMAG – Joint U.S. Military Advisory Group

MCSC – Managed Care Support Contactor

MHS – Military Health System

MoH – Medal of Honor

MTF – Military Treatment Facility

OHI – Other Health Insurance

OMSC – Overseas Military Services Coordinator

OSA – Obstructive Sleep Apnea

OTC – Over the Counter (drugs)

P&T – Permanent & Total Disability (VA classification)

PCM - Primary Care Manager

pf – per family

PLDT – Philippine Long-Distance Telephone

POS – Point of Service

pp – per person

PSA – Prime Service Area

QLE – Qualifying Life Event

RACHAP/RHAPP – Retiree-At-Cost Hearing Aid Program/Retiree Hearing Aid Purchase Program

RAO – Retired Activities Office

SOFA – Status of Forces Agreement

SSA – Social Security Administration

SSN – Social Security Number

TAMP - Transitional Assistance Management Program

TDP – TRICARE Dental Program

TFL – TRICARE for Life

TOP – TRICARE Overseas Program

TRR – TRICARE Retired Reserve

TRS – TRICARE Reserve Select

TSC – TRICARE Service Center

TYA – TRICARE Young Adult

TYA-S – TRICARE Young Adult-Select

TYA-P – TRICARE Young Adult-Prime

USFHP – United States Family Health Plan

USMTF – United States Military Treatment Facility

VA – (Department of) Veterans Affairs

VFW – Veterans of Foreign Wars

VSI – Voluntary Separation Incentive

VSO – Veterans Service Organizations

WPS - Wisconsin Physician Service

Appendix C:
Age-Related TRICARE Events

THE FOLLOWING ARE TRICARE EVENTS based on age. Details can be found in the cross-referenced sections listed for each event.

Age 0 (newborn): Auto-enrolled in TRICARE Prime, Prime Remote or Select based on location and status of parents.
Reference: Chapter 2, "Newborns"

Age 90 days (stateside) or 120 days (overseas): Deadline for DEERS enrollment for continuous coverage under TRICARE.
Reference: Chapter 2, "Newborns"

Age 21 (or 23, if enrolled full-time as a college student): Cut-off for coverage under sponsor's plan.
Reference: Chapter 2, "Adult Children"

Age 21: Deadline to certify adult children with significant disabilities to remain on parent's TRICARE plan.
Reference: Chapter 2, "Adult Children with Disabilities"

Age 26: Cut-off for coverage under TRICARE Young Adult.
Reference: Chapter 6, "TRICARE Young Adult"

Age 60: For gray area retirees and their dependents, transition from TRICARE Retired Reserve to TRICARE Prime or Select.
Reference: Chapter 6, "TRICARE Retired Reserve"

Age 65: Transition to TRICARE for Life for all TRICARE beneficiaries. Exceptions apply for active duty members or active duty family members.
Reference: Chapter 6, "TRICARE for Life"

Appendix D:
TRICARE Claim Checklist

THIS IS YOUR "ONE-STOP CHECKLIST" for filing your claims with TRICARE. These tips come from TRICARE Overseas (ISOS), **Tricare.mil**, and the TRICARE claim form itself (DD-2642). Many of these tips are deeply hidden in these websites and appear only after you fill out your online claim.

Carefully following these steps will avoid 99% of the reasons that claims are commonly denied. Do not take shortcuts or work from memory; read the checklist each time. If you do so, you can expect most claims to be approved in just a few weeks.

1. **Follow TRICARE's own filing tips.** *__Reference__:* **tricare.mil/FormsClaims/Claims/MedicalClaims/FilingTips**

   a. Keep DEERS current and complete for all family members, especially after an address change or changes in your family (e.g., birth, adoption, marriage, divorce, death). Incorrect information in DEERS can cause your claim to be delayed or denied.

   b. Use form DD-2642 to file your claim. The form can be downloaded from **tricare.mil** or from your regional contractor's website.

   c. Fill in all 12 boxes fully and accurately.

   d. List the diagnosis code in Block 8a. If unknown, state a full description of the reason for care in Block 8a.

   e. Sign the form! Claims submitted without a signature will be denied payment.

f. If you were injured by another party, whether intentional or accidental, you <u>must</u> let TRICARE know by including DD Form 2527 (Statement of Personal Injury). See Chapter 11, "Third Party Liability" for more about this.

g. File claims with Other Health Insurance (OHI) first. You must include the OHI explanation of benefits (EOB) when you submit your TRICARE claim. **Failing to settle OHI first constitutes insurance fraud and is subject to prosecution!**

h. **Keep copies of everything.** Documents can and do get lost during filing.

i. Send claims to the right address. One processor will not forward to another if you send it to the wrong one. See the section in Chapter 11: "Who Do You File With?"

j. File on time. You have one year to file for care received in the States; **three years for care received overseas**.

k. Submit each claim separately. Bundling multiple claims together is likely to cause confusion.

l. Pat yourself on the back for a job well done.

2. **Who do you file with?**

a. **If you are enrolled with TRICARE Overseas,** file with TRICARE Overseas even if you get care in the U.S. *Reference:* http://www.tricare-overseas.com/ beneficiaries/resources/traveling-beneficiaries

b. **If you are enrolled in a stateside TRICARE plan and get medical care overseas**, file with TRICARE Overseas (not with your U.S. regional contractor). This is true for all TRICARE beneficiaries. *Reference:* https://tricare.mil/FormsClaims/ Claims/MedicalClaims/FilingOverseas

c. **If you are enrolled in a stateside plan and get medical care in a different region** (for example, you are in TRICARE East but get care in the West region), file with your home regional contractor.

3. **Digital file format for online claims:**

- **Scan in grayscale or black & white, not color.** The TOP claim processing system is incapable of handling color attachments. Research your scanner's instructions to learn how to do this; each is different. **Even a black & white document should not be scanned in color** because the resulting file format is different than a grayscale scan. If you are notified that an attachment is missing or unreadable, this is probably the reason why. *Reference:* Pop-up window <u>after</u> submitting attachments on the TOP portal.

- **When submitting electronically, put all of the documents into a single multi-page file.** This includes the doctor's report, hospital bill, credit card receipt, DD-2642, etc. While the portal allows upload of multiple attachments, they warn you not to do so, and claims can be rejected for this reason. On a Mac, you can combine documents into a single PDF file using the Preview app. On a Windows computer, you will need third-party software to combine documents. You also can paste scanned documents into Word or PowerPoint and upload it as a .doc or .ppt file.

- **File size should not exceed 8 MB.** This may be difficult if you have many scanned documents. If it is impossible to fit everything in less than 8 MB via the portal, upload what you can and attach the rest to the confirmation message in your Message Center. Make sure the message includes your claim number. The additional documents will be added to your claim. Wait 24 hours, and then call to double-check that everything arrived.

4. **Block 8A is your friend!** Use Block 8A on form DD-2642 to explain why you or a family member needed care. If your claim is not clear on why the treatment was needed, it may be rejected.

If you cannot fit full details in Block 8A, it might be best to write: "See attached page." On a separate sheet, take as much room as you need to explain the reason for the care. Do not assume the reviewer knows anything of your prior history; make it easy for them to understand. Do NOT try to write as little as possible; that is the fast-track for a claim to be rejected.

5. Annotate/Mark Up Your Documents

a. At the top of your claim form, write **"Beneficiary Paid Provider Directly"** and **the amount paid**. This makes clear that you already paid the bill and TRICARE should reimburse you, not the hospital. For more information, see **www.tricare.mil/proofofpayment**.

b. At the top of all other pages, write the patient's name and the sponsor's SSN or DBN. **_Reference_**: Item #7 of "Reminders" on page 1 of DD-2642.

c. Check box 13 (currency). Check "Yes" if you want to receive a check in local currency (e.g., Euros, pesos, baht, yen, etc.). Check "No" if you want to be paid in U.S. dollars. Not all currencies are available, so call ISOS if you have questions.

6. Document translation is optional.
ISOS will accept documents in a foreign language, but you may prefer to ask your provider to provide the medical report in English. At a minimum, ensure that the patient's name is written using English (Latin) characters, not transliterated into a foreign alphabet. Japanese, for example, has a special alphabet (_katakana_) to show the Japanese phonetic pronunciation of foreign words. Writing your name in _katakana_ can cause problems with claims processing, so ask the provider to write your name in English.

7. Pay with plastic.
Paying medical bills with cash can be a red flag for potential fraud. If you do pay with cash, be prepared for longer processing time and more scrutiny. Submit ATM or bank receipts with your claim to show the cash withdrawal. If possible,

pay with a credit card or debit card to avoid this complication. See our discussion of this in Chapter 8, in the section "Pay with Plastic."

8. **Follow-up.** After submitting your claim, wait at least 24 hours and then call to ensure that it was correctly received. The questions to ask when you call:

    a. Was my claim received?

    b. What pages do you see? *(Have your copies ready so you can compare.)*

    c. Are all the pages legible? *(Sometimes they get garbled if sent via the portal.)*

    d. Do you see any problems? *(The representative should check the entire claim for obvious errors or problems. This is not a guarantee of approval, but it can head off problems early in the process.)*

    e. Confirm that the reimbursement will come to you, not to the provider – if you paid the provider directly.

We have found the service representatives to be quite helpful during these reviews. If they tell you that an attachment is garbled or missing, you do not have to re-submit the entire claim. Create a message in the Message Center with the subject "General Question", write the Claim Number in the body of your message, and attach the file. The new file should automatically be appended to your existing claim, but never assume. Call back the next business day to make sure that it was received and added to your claim.

9. **Seek assistance.** There are many excellent resources to assist with your claim. This includes customer representatives at the **TRICARE Overseas regional offices**. They are available by phone 24 hours, Monday through Friday, in their local time zone, so you do not have to call in the middle of the night.

Retired Activities Offices (RAO) around the world can help or will refer you to appropriate resources. **VFW posts and**

other veterans' groups often have subject matter experts to help. Seek them out.

At major military bases around the world, you will find **TRICARE Service Centers (TSC)** for face-to-face assistance with questions or with completing and submitting claims. They are also knowledgeable about health care options off base, which can be particularly helpful to those on TRICARE Select who do not have a PCM to give referrals.

Chapter 12 has contact information for these groups and more. Review this chapter thoroughly to find a wide range of free assistance worldwide.

10. **Join our Facebook group *"TRICARE Around the World"*** to connect with thousands of military members, retirees, families, and caregivers worldwide. You will be able to interact with the author and group experts. We are committed to providing fast, reliable information to all who ask.

Once you join, you will find other resources, including groups for **TRICARE in Thailand, Germany, and the Philippines**, plus **TRICARE for new moms and moms-to-be.** For links to these groups, plus other ways to find assistance worldwide, visit **www.theTRICARE.guy.com**. On that page, you can sign up for our mailing list to get info on new revisions of this book and how to receive special deals and discounts in the future.

Stay Involved!

Through the *TRICARE Around the World* community, we are trying to make life better for our military family. Here are some things you can do to help:

- PLEASE go back to the site where you bought this book and **post a 5-star review**. A paragraph or two from you helps lift this book in the search results, allowing us to reach even more in the military community.

- **Visit www.theTRICAREguy.com to join our mailing list.** Send us your ideas on how to make future editions of this book even better. We welcome your input. This edition addresses a range of feedback from readers like you.

- Check our website for **the latest edition of this book.** We plan to update it periodically both in digital (eBook) form and in paperback. We want you to get the most from the benefits that you have <u>earned</u> through your military service. Stay current and stay healthy...and tell your friends about us!

- **Join our global community.** Our Facebook group is not just a place to ask questions, but also to share with others what you have learned about your TRICARE benefits. Our community needs you!

See you online and on your global travels!

www.theTRICAREguy.com

About the Author

John D. Letaw is a retired Naval officer who served on six different ships in the Pacific fleet throughout his career. Later, as a defense contractor, he helped to develop and deploy tactical software to ensure mission success for Joint forces. From 2009-2012, in Iwakuni, Japan, John served as the Asia-Pacific Regional Manager of the Transition Assistance Program (TAP), teaching classes in career transition, and counseling military members and their spouses about life after the military. During that time, John and his wife Pen also ran a youth program at the station chapel.

In retirement, John turned his attention to TRICARE and how to make it accessible to all. This effort sprang from his family's nomadic lifestyle, which gave them deep insight into using TRICARE health benefits in a variety of settings – from remote mountain villages in Japan to gleaming 5-star hospitals in Bangkok, as a SOFA-status contractor overseas, and as a retiree in Hawaii.

John's Facebook group, *TRICARE Around the World,* is the world's largest and most active online community dedicated to sharing information about TRICARE. With 10,000 members and growing, the questions, stories, setbacks, and victories shared in the group has had a profound influence on the development of this book.

For links to our community or to sign up for our newsletter, visit the author's website at www.TheTricareGuy.com